Derek Macfarlane is an electrical engineer, who spent 16 years helping software engineers develop the IT functions that have become ADMS. His role included technical advice on how the electricity industry operates its networks, assistance with bids and sales of ADMS around the world. The software product itself developed from single applications to the suite of applications involved in ADMS today. He gained experience of electricity utilities on every continent, and during this time, he wrote and co-authored several papers relating to DMS published by CIRED, CIGRE and IEEE. Prior to that, he spent 32 years working as an engineer and middle manager in electricity distribution and was a manager in the 1990s when the UK industry was being privatised. Privatisation introduced the drive to reduce costs and increase performance, and these influences opened up the industry to computerisation of their business processes. His last few years in the electricity industry were spent attempting to improve an in-house Outage Management software system (OMS). The experience and limitations of the traditional mainframe environment that hosted OMS, served to convince him that a modern solution, available from external IT vendors, was the correct way forward. He was then involved in specifying the replacement OMS, selecting the vendor and introducing the IT system into their operational environment. Having spent most of his engineering career designing, building operating and fault finding on the live HV, MV and LV networks, the opportunity to step back and analyse the business processes and seek better procedures with improved consistency in performance, efficiency and reliability was a refreshing intellectual and business challenge.

The electricity industry is correctly obsessed with safety, working as it does with potentially lethal voltages. There has always been an impressive safety regime, learning from mistakes and errors, always with a view to understand the cause and avoid repetition. This created a culture of observance of safety procedures, risk assessment and risk management throughout the industry from managers to tradesmen. The introduction of new technology and new procedures had to be implemented into this safety-first environment, and this presented challenges in ensuring the new technology recognised the safety implications of their proposed new methods and provided full and complete provision of the same level of safety that the old procedures were there to ensure. All change in such an environment includes risk, it is normal to find resistance to any change, from staff who can be held responsible for errors, mistakes, injuries and deaths. Therefore, it is fitting to recognise the dedication and professionalism of the utility industry staff who helped test, improve and deploy ADMS into a very challenging operational environment.

When I moved from the electricity industry into the software industry, I was 50 and everyone in the company I joined was under 40, even the company directors. I met a bunch of young software engineers and they are the brightest people I have ever had the privilege of working with. Writing software is a brutally rigorous, discipline, if the software engineer does not anticipate every possible outcome and include software instructions on how to deal with each of them, then the computer just stops, possibly sends an error message and waits to be told what to do. Now multiply that by the thousands of lines of code in each of the ADMS functions, and I stand in awe of the skill, dedication, concentration and organisation displayed by software engineers.

Assisting Understanding

One cannot write about IT systems without entering acronym hell, and a simple dictionary entry cannot impart the full meaning of the acronyms. Therefore, in section three, the major acronyms are each described explaining their purpose.

Derek Macfarlane

An Introduction to ADMS

The Operation, Command and
Control of Electricity
Distribution Networks

Austin Macauley Publishers™
London • Cambridge • New York • Sharjah

A CIP catalogue record for this title is available from the British Library.

ISBN 9781398406018 (Paperback)
ISBN 9781398406025 (ePub e-book)

www.austinmacauley.com

First Published 2021
Austin Macauley Publishers Ltd®
1 Canada Square
Canary Wharf
London
E14 5AA
+44 (0)20 7038 8212
+44 (0)20 3515 0352

Table of Contents

1 Introduction   **11**

2 The Purpose of DMS and ADMS   **14**

2.1 A Cautionary Note   *14*

2.2 Definitions of DMS and ADMS   *15*

3 DMS Functions and Their Purpose   **18**

3.1 DMS   *19*

3.2 NMS   *21*

3.3 OMS   *26*

3.4 SCADA   *29*

3.5 Mobile   *33*

3.6 On Line Network Analysis   *36*

3.6.1 Load Profiles   *41*

3.6.2 The Effect of Embedded Renewable Energy on Distribution Networks   *43*

3.7 DPF (Distribution Power Flow) Load Flow Calculation   *47*

3.8 Fault Level Calculation SCC (Short Circuit alculation)   *49*

3.9 DTF   *49*

3.10 FDIR Fault Detection, Isolation & Restoration   *50*

3.11 ANM 52

3.12 IVVC 53

3.13 Reports 53

4 Data Storage in ADMS **56**

4.1 RDBMS 56

4.2 RTDB 57

4.3 Historian Real Time Data Store 58

4.4 Reports DB 58

5 The Interaction of DMS with Other Corporate IT Systems **60**

5.1 EMS 60

5.2 CRM 62

5.3 GIS 63

5.4 AMS 66

5.5 SMMS 67

5.6 Embedded Renewable Generation 69

6 Maintenance of DMS **70**

6.1 Operational Updates of the Network Data 72

6.1.1 Time Warp Errors 73

6.2 Connectivity Errors 85

6.3 Potential Connectivity Errors in ADMS Update Processes 89

6.4 Summary of Data Maintenance in ADMS 92

6.5 Maintenance of the Generic IT Aspects of ADMS 93

7 Non Functional Requirements of DMS **96**

7.1 Flexible Architecture and Deployment 96

7.2 Reliability and Resilience 98

7.3 Back Up Tapes of DMS Transactions 99

7.4 Real Time Performance 99

7.5 Productised Software 101

7.6 Integrated Systems 105

7.7 Tolerance of Poor or Missing Data 108

8 Extracting Added Value from ADMS **111**

8.1 ADMS Data 111

8.2 Data Configuration 113

8.3 Interface and/or Reports into Asset Management 114

8.4 Interface with Smart Meter Management Systems (MMS) 115

8.5 The Improved Management of the LV Network 117

8.6 The Achievement of Real Time Truth 121

9 ADMS Yesterday, Today and Tomorrow **123**

1

Introduction

This book is intended to be read by the electricity industry staff who are looking for IT systems to improve their electricity distribution processes and network performance.

I was once challenged by a utility manager, who had as their aim to be the best distribution business in their region. "How can you make us the best if you only sell us the same software you sell everyone else?"

My answer used a domestic analogy. "Consider a street lined with houses and front gardens. All the householders have similar garden tools, yet some gardens are much nicer than others. The differences are twofold: first, you must have a clear understanding of what tools to buy and what conditions to create to enable you to compete with the best, and secondly, it is in the skill and knowledge you apply to get the best out of your tools that makes the difference. These newly required IT skills are the modern differentiators between electricity utilities. Those who understand their IT investments, how to maintain them, how to get the best out of them and how to keep the data up to date and accurate, these are the utilities with benchmark levels of performance for their type of network."

I helped to sell ADMS to electricity companies around the world for 16 years, and from my experience many companies become confused in what they want, they may be influenced by previous investment decisions which slant their assessment of what they need for an ADMS. They are obliged to make decisions between technologies without having the prior experience of different outcomes from different solutions. Over these years, I have been involved in wins and losses of contracts and, the joys of winning apart, the most informative moments were in discovering why we lost. Sometimes, we lost for what we perceived to be good justifiable reasons and in others we were prepared to bet we would be getting a second bite at that opportunity a few more years down the track and happily we converted several of those at the second time of asking.

I have tried to prevent this book from becoming a plug for one solution. It discusses several options at various junctures through the topics and hopefully explains the differences between some of the key technology decisions, dispel some of the myths and seek practical workable solutions. I look at various options and attempt to explain my way through the technical quagmire towards the solution that is best fit for each customer.

Then, having spent millions to buy an ADMS, many utilities do not use it to its full advantage. To use another analogy, having bought a fancy sports car they only drive it in third gear. In this book, I hope to enable the power engineers with a better understanding of the IT industry, the relevant IT applications and how to get the best out of their investments.

In writing a book, I am in effect taking a photograph of a dynamic and fluid process. This process is continually developing and ADMS is continuing to develop as the challenges, ideas and operational experience also evolve. However, the book is needed as a baseline of what we currently can do and where we want to go.

2

The Purpose of DMS
and ADMS

2.1 A Cautionary Note

The IT vendors each use the acronyms DMS and ADMS, Distribution Management System and Advanced DMS, for their own purposes, there is no standard definition of what is an ADMS or a DMS, so most vendors claim they have one. Potential customer utilities need to have an enquiring attitude and a firm concept of their business needs prior to selection of their chosen vendor/product. IT systems are expensive to buy and complicated to maintain. The only way of ensuring value for money is to pursue a strict business benefit case for each function. The IT industry is an ideas factory, and many ideas look good on the screen, but some of these are just technical nice to haves if they do not have a primary justification in a costed business case.

Volvo has an advertisement for the XC40 with the tagline, 'Everything you need, nothing you don't', and this implies that IT for cars is in a similar position to ADMS in that technology can now offer a lot, and the blind rush into the newest available is now needing to be replaced with rigorous process, users and needs analyses. New IT features may distract Volvo drivers from their prime task which is driving safely, similarly new functions in ADMS can distract or divert the control engineer into interesting and diverting insights but lose track of the main function of controlling the network and operating safely.

What is the business process being modelled?

How many distinct types of user are involved in the process?

Which users need which features?

What would happen if the feature was not available?

2.2 Definitions of DMS and ADMS

An initial definition for DMS, it is the IT system which is used for operation and control of the electricity distribution networks, that is networks operating at high voltage (HV, 132kV down to 20kV), medium voltage (MV, 20kV down to 1kV) and low voltage (LV, below 1,000volts), ending on customers premises with a terminal protection device and a meter. This includes interfaces passing real time information between DMS other business processes affected by real time operations. Typical users of this system and its data are:

Control engineers, outage planners, outage dispatchers, operating crews, customer call takers, SCADA maintenance staff, data maintenance staff, diagram maintenance staff, reports users, general management, regulatory management, customer management, asset management, major incident management and IT management.

An initial definition of ADMS: it productises DMS within the full asset management lifecycle and adds the productised interactions with Asset Management Systems, Geospatial Information Systems, and other corporate IT systems to ensure consistency of data between systems and seamless interaction from 'back office' (design, asset strategy and management) and 'front office' (live network operations in DMS).

Typical users of ADMS include most of the DMS users, plus GIS data maintenance staff, asset managers, GIS based network designers and planners.

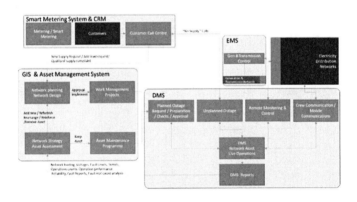

Figure 1: DMS within the ADMS Larger Picture of a Distribution Company

DMS is all about operating the assets connected to the live distribution network:

- Responding to requests from project engineers to connect new assets to the network.

- Responding to requests from maintenance engineers to isolate items of plant for maintenance.
- Responding to unplanned events affecting the network, such as storm damage, network-initiated alarms and events.
- Interacting with transmission control.
- Ensuring the distribution network is operated safely and kept stable.
- Ensuring crews who operate switches or work on the network, do so with safety as the prime focus.
- Ensuring the public is kept safe from the potential dangers from electricity networks.
- Providing customers with the most reliable supply practicable.
- Providing customers with the quality and amounts of power on demand, within pre-agreed limits and within the standards.

The DMS, therefore, is a collection of functions essential to supporting control engineers in the safe management of the network, the reliable delivery of electricity to customers and the safe deployment of crews who are switching or working on the network.

3

DMS Functions and Their Purpose

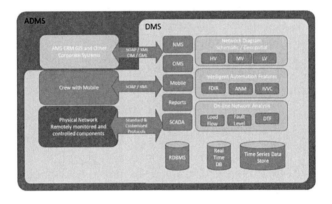

Figure 2: Development of DMS Functions from 1991 to 2016

Figure 2 shows a block diagram of typical DMS functions available today. The immediate understanding of this diagram requires an acronym dictionary, and the descriptions follow in the next section. However, each ADMS vendor would produce their own block diagram and it will hold clues as to how each vendor's system is put together. For instance, it may show OMS and or SCADA as an interfaced product rather than being embedded in DMS and this tends to imply that their OMS or SCADA has been developed separately, it may not be their own product, possibly a commercial arrangement with a third-party specialist function provider, or indeed these products might have been purchased and brought into the common stable of functions provided by the vendor. In essence, they are separate products with their own unique software but have been custom interfaced into the vendor's stable product. Some vendors have all or most of these components within the one software version, as licenced modules within a single DMS software suite developed as an integrated system.

3.1 DMS

The major real time business processes that needed to be modelled in DMS are:

- The management of safety as crews operate switches on the network and as crews are set to work.
- Managing the network model as used in the control room in a manner that always reflects the actual state of the real network.
- Managing the unplanned outages and organising the response, investigation and recovery.
- Managing the operational work including requests for outages for new connections or for maintenance.
- Managing the loading of every component of the network as it attempts to meet the demand of customers.

These processes are not mutually exclusive, there are situations where they interact, for instance, SCADA remotely operating a switch requires to also be controlled and recorded as part of switching management, but its data acquisition role feeds into the load management process. SCADA sensing a fault and tripping a circuit breaker requires to be recorded in both the switching management process and the unplanned outage management process. The planning of switching outages requires to check the prospective loading of the adjacent circuits affected by the temporary abnormal feeding arrangement and, therefore, involves elements of the load management process.

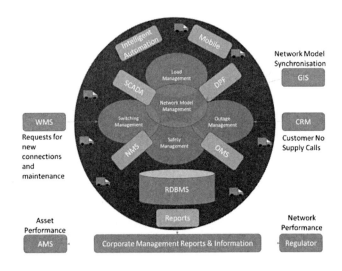

Figure 3: The interrelationships between the major operational processes and the ADMS functions

3.2 NMS

NMS is the Network Management System. This has four major parts:

- Modelling the network.
- Updating that model in real time.
- The management of planned and unplanned switching on the network.
- The management of safety documentation.

There are several network models that can be used, a geospatially accurate model found in the GIS, a schematic network model, (the electrical equivalent of the London underground map,) and a geo-schematic which accepts some geospatial inputs to assist in orientation within a schematic model. For operations purposes, the schematic provides the clearest representation of electrical connectivity and the current state of switches and other network components. The schematic is, therefore, used for HV and MV networks, the LV network, due to its massive size is usually a geo-schematic based on the GIS geospatial record of the LV assets. There is no other reason other than clarity of connectivity, to use a schematic at HV and MV and indeed most US utilities do use a geospatial or geo-schematic model for their MV network, because the polar orientations are often used by crews to identify where they are operating.

The lower the voltage the higher the involvement of crews on site in switching and working on the networks. EHV transmission networks are important, but relatively small and work tends to be done on the basis of large contracts with only a final test and connection to the live system. The volume of these changes tends to be single figures, under ten major additions/changes per year. This relatively low level of disturbance meant that the EHV control systems (EMS) tended to ignore model change as a regular process and allowed one off changes to be inserted in a relatively manual bespoke process. The HV network is larger and the MV network is ten to one hundred times larger than EHV and the corresponding amount of work on the network also increases. This produces a workload of thousands of network additions and changes per year, and, therefore, NMS requires a business process to manage the introduction of changes to the model. A major requirement of this business process is that it keeps the model accurate in real time so that the control engineer and the site personnel both understand the current connectivity of the network. Changes to the schematic operational control diagram must be implemented in real time and within a business process that provides those responsible for safety, the control engineers, with a means of prechecking and approval prior to implementation. NMS includes this process within its functions.

Switching management is the major activity going on in a distribution control centre. This can take several forms:

- Manually initiated, remotely controlled automated switching by the control engineer.
- Manual switching, planned in advance, under direct command from control engineer to an onsite operative, who may be an engineer a linesman or other operationally qualified tradesman.

- Manual switching as an unplanned response to an unexpected network event.
- Intelligent automation driven switching triggered by an unexpected network event.
- Manual and or automatic network adjustment in response to dynamic network conditions such as voltage levels or loading constraints.

NMS should manage all five forms in one consistent set of switching logs. Each switching log identifies what type of job is ongoing and has a unique identifier number. The switching log requires to identify the substation name, the switch name, the type of operation undertaken, the operator's ID, the control engineer's ID and the relevant timings of each instruction. The timings include time of instruction, and time confirmed complete.

Switching logs for EMS EHV controls tend to be one log per control engineer, however, to manage the massive amount of switching done at HV and MV in distribution control rooms NMS usually provides a filing system of switching schedules, and each control engineer manages around 20 or so switching schedules per shift. Switching schedules can be created and checked in advance for known events such as an outage for maintenance of existing network components or for the addition of new network components such as a new substation supplying a new factory or housing estate. Control engineers can also keep available a switching log for dynamic switching in response to network constraints similar to the EHV switching log, and also the distribution control engineer can create a new switching log on the fly as faults occur and they wish to capture all the relevant switching within the one log which describes the network loss and recovery actions all in the one file.

These switching schedules can cope with both switching initiated by the control engineer using the SCADA remote control functions and the control engineer issuing instructions to a site crew for manual implementation. SCADA switching tends to be instructed acknowledged and confirmed complete within a few seconds, whereas the manual communication and confirmation process is bound by safety rules to help ensure accurate communication between control and crew and minimise human error. This manual process is necessary because not all distribution switches are automatic or connected to SCADA and there are operational actions that SCADA cannot control such as safety isolation and earthing.

Safety documentation is a legally required precaution when people are asked to work or carry out tasks in potentially hazardous environments. Electricity networks which are, or were, live at medium or high voltage (over 1,000v), are identified as being sufficiently hazardous to require formal safety documentation to be prepared prior to tasks commencing. The NMS function 'polices' the current network state and has safety logic which identifies when the network is fully isolated and earthed such that safety documents can be issued to enable testing or work to be undertaken. Permits to Work (PTW), Sanction for Test (SFT), and Limitations of Access (LOA), are three of the more regularly used safety documents, although there are more. Each document requires the network to be in a specific state prior to issue, each document closely defines the tasks which may be done under the cover of the document, and defines in detail where on the network these tasks can be done. The needs of each document differ, a PTW requires the section of network, upon which work is to be done, to be isolated from each and every possible source of supply and must be bounded by earthed points between the point of work and any sources of supply. These earths may not be disturbed during the life of the PTW. An SFT requires the same starting conditions but, since testing is to be done, it must be possible to apply a test voltage to the isolated section, so it is acceptable within the life of an SFT to remove the earths so that test voltages can be applied. These are just examples of how safety documents each restrict actions in their own distinct ways. An LOA enables crews to work in proximity to live network assets, but not within the safety clearances. They can control the routes crews take when approaching their worksite and restrict them from carrying ladders etc. which might touch overhead live conductors. Tree cutting by contractors is often also covered by LOA documentation, provided the trees themselves are not already encroaching on the safety clearances to the overhead lines. These documents have a legal role, and are amongst the first items of evidence asked for in the event of an accident or fatality. NMS includes safety logic to assess if the network is in the correct state to allow the issue of safety documents and records their issue and cancellation so that a formal electronic record is available of their use. The prime documents are still physical paper documents handed out to working crews by senior authorised people who have been trained and assessed as competent to set up safe zones of work and ensure the initiation of work is done rigorously with a full understanding of the work to be done and the limits within which the work must be kept.

The final part of NMS functionality relates to its interaction with other aspects of DMS. Intelligent automation features can identify unplanned outages, ascertain the scope of the outage and the location of a fault within one particular network section and then assess and automate the restoration around that faulty section. NMS responds automatically to capture the actions of this intelligent automation and makes a record of the automated restoration within a specially created switching log. An unplanned outage on the distribution network often affects customer supplies and in these cases, NMS also interacts with OMS and supplies the relevant times and switching actions into the OMS event log. NMS can also be used to invoke DPF network load flow calculations during the outage planning phase of preparation of switching logs and can also be invoked dynamically during the implementation of the switching schedule.

3.3 OMS

OMS is the Outage Management System. It, too, is concerned with both planned and unplanned outages, but its major focus is on organising the internal response within the utility, minimising customer outages and keeping control of each outage through its investigation/restoration/repair lifecycle.

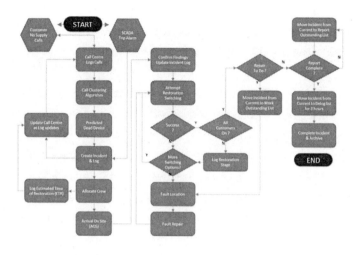

Figure 4: OMS Business Process Flow Chart

NMS focused on the network, OMS focuses on customers' restoration of supplies. OMS came into its own as a product for helping to deal with major storms, keeping track of all the outages and restoring them in an order that prioritised customers. Planned outages uses the OMS functionality to pre-warn customers of impending planned work which requires to interfere with their electricity supply. OMS, therefore, sits as a function between the customer call centre(s), the control room(s), and the crew despatch centre(s), and interacts with all three organisations. OMS is a real-time function in that the operators have to react to real time events and make real time decisions and implement them. OMS, therefore, can either be informed of an outage via a SCADA tripped circuit breaker or by input from the call centre where incoming customer calls are reporting losses of supply. Both sources of data are necessary because SCADA typically does not cover all the possible protection points on the MV network, and in these cases the systems depend upon a cluster analysis of incoming customer calls to ascertain the scope of the outage and probable protection tripping point. SCADA reports are firm data, and these can be used to create confirmed incidents. Customer call data is just used to infer the probable size of the outage. This data can be confused, it may be several smaller outages or all one big outage and, in the absence of other confirmations, OMS considers these inferred incidents as 'predicted' and the first action is to allocate a crew to investigate on site and confirm the finding. OMS is then updated by the crew (either directly using a Mobile device or indirectly by contacting the OMS dispatcher who updates the OMS). The generic process thereafter is to isolate the fault, restore as many customers as possible by alternate supply arrangements, and then to repair the fault and restore the network back to normal. The OMS incident can be removed from the 'current' incident list after all customers are restored. This can be before repair of the fault, provided there is a full alternative supply available, or it may mean restoring the last few customers after repair because there is no alternative source for these customers. OMS data is presented in summaries, dashboard displays and as symbols and colour schemes applied to a network diagram model. Again, this can be either schematic or geospatial or both. Data from OMS is then used to calculate the reliability statistics for the distribution network and this is usually done via the IEEE standard metrics relating to the frequency of outages and a second metric relating to the duration of outages, CAIFI CAIDI, SAIFI SAIDI referring to Customer Average Interruption Frequency Index and CAI Duration Index and the same calculations based on the System Average Interruption Index and duration index. These reported metrics are very important because they are the basis for the reward or penalty to the utility for the reliability of supply provided to customers and this can affect their profitability by several million dollars either way.

3.4 SCADA

SCADA is the System Control and Data Acquisition function. SCADA is the oldest function and is usually the first IT based application used in a control room. SCADA has a dedicated communication network to Remote Terminal Units (RTUs) sited in the substations where analogue sensors collect voltage and current (amps) data from strategic points within the substation and network, convert them to a digital format (organised in a specific protocol) and communicate this data back to a Front-End Processor (FEP) and from there back into the SCADA server. The illustration shows two Primary Substations each with an RTU collecting data from the transformers and circuit breakers plus the ability to remotely operate the circuit breakers and the tap change controller, fans and pumps on each primary transformer. Also illustrated is a typical deployment of SCADA to enable intelligent automation from intermediate switches along MV feeders. The RTUs at primary substations can collect data or control from some 200 different points, the RTUs at selected secondary substations typically have up to 50 points configured as data or control points. The rural network can also include intelligent automation, although not illustrated here. Note also the multiple redundancy capability of the master servers connected to a dual redundant WAN, dual redundancy at FEP level and the ability of each FEP pair to have multiple communications lines with multi dropped RTUs along each route. This is a typical arrangement to allow for the massive MV network spread across several hundreds of square miles. Communication options are not limited, they include copper wire, radio, mobile phone networks, optical fibre, internet protocol and satellite communications.

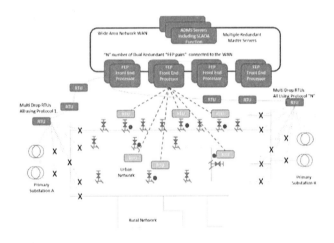

Figure 5: Typical SCADA Hardware and Communications Infrastructure.

SCADA has three main functions:

1. A Monitoring Function

The collection of measurements, from the remote network sites are stored in a special real time database. In this database other points can be derived by preconfigured sets of calculations and the derived points are also stored in the real time database. The DMS has the option to display some or all of this data in meaningful locations across the network diagram model, and the data can also be siphoned off into a historical database where the points do not overwrite themselves every scan, but stack themselves, either as they are or converted into, say half hour averages, to provide a historical archive of loads and voltages. Once a complete set of data has been scanned from the network, the next scan commences repeating the process in a matter of seconds. To avoid massive amounts of duplication, should the new scan reading be similar to the last then it is not transmitted, there is a tolerance limit set and once the reading is sufficiently different from the last scanned figure the new figure is returned as a refreshed measurement.

2. An Alarm Function

An alarm mechanism applied to the measurements to sift out the data that is close to or breaching pre-set limits. For instance this can be a current limit applicable to a certain size of cable to ensure that the cable is not overloaded and overheated as a result. Regular cycles of overheating or a single event of extreme overheating can shorten the asset life of the cable, or destroy it. Alarms were devised to draw the engineer's attention to matters requiring action. As SCADA has extended its deployment across HV and partially across MV, the numbers of alarms can become very large. In addition to this other functions such as OMS and DPF load flow analysis can also generate alarms. The alarm screen in a modern ADMS has sorting and filtering and classification of alarms plus the ability for different types of users to access the alarms of particular interest to their role. For instance a control engineer managing the North district of the network can have their system configured to only show north district alarms. The South district OMS operator can have their system configured to only show OMS type alarms within South District. An alarm, once raised has to be acknowledged by an operator. That action of acknowledgment can also be made to be a trigger in the continuity process, leading the engineer on to relate the alarm to an existing known fault job or prompting the creation of a new job. It is functions like this which enable new inexperienced control engineers to be drawn along into the processes just as effectively as experienced operators.

3. A Remote Control Function

A control function enabling control engineers to send commands to operate a switch and receive confirmations of that command being completed or aborted. Also SCADA detects unsolicited switching events which occur on the network, usually caused by the protection systems detecting a fault occurrence via some protection device and immediately tripping the circuit breaker. These 'unsolicited trips' are sent back to the SCADA system as priority messages and appear on the Alarm screen of the operator's console.

SCADA is used widely across the EHV and HV networks but due to the relative expense of deploying communications and sensors, it is only partially deployed across MV networks and some LV networks. This is why DMS includes other functions, to compensate for incomplete SCADA coverage at

MV and LV. SCADA predates DMS in its development, therefore, there are many SCADA systems still in use today that are effectively standalone applications, and DMS or ADMS operate around them with a set of interfaces to interact between the SCADA system and the wider DMS functions. Modern DMS however, also includes embedded and totally integrated SCADA as part of the DMS functions.

Historically, SCADA systems were proprietorial, the vendor developed the RTUs, and the bespoke protocol language used for communication, their own FEPs and their own SCADA master stations. Everything had to be obtained from the same vendor. In the 1990s, these 'proprietorial traps' were sprung by the first generation of universal SCADA systems which utilised libraries of protocols to communicate with many different vendors' RTUs. These new systems communicated to all the vendors' RTUs, by selecting that particular protocol from its library prior to scan the data from that vendors RTUs. The new system required to replace the old vendor specific master stations and FEPS with modern DMS servers and modern dual redundant FEPs which could control multiple different proprietary SCADA installations. The modernisation became a practical proposition because most of the RTUs and communication lines could be reused by the modern ADMS SCADA function and thereby avoided a major potential cost of refitting.

3.5 Mobile

Mobile systems enable crews to be included within the users who can benefit from access to the DMS operational environment. However, due to the IT security, and the strong safety culture necessary within electricity distribution, the types of mobile system suitable for operational work are restricted to those which can support the strict communication requirements that exist particularly between control and crews involved in switching management. Typically systems that 'broadcast' over the internet fail to meet the requirements of proof of receipt of a message, proof of understanding, and the corresponding rigour during the crews' confirmation of actions taken. The second major requirement is sufficient speed to be comparable with the present speech messaging between control and crews. Thirdly the mobile requires an interface capable of being operated by crews operating in difficult outdoor conditions, therefore, delicate manoeuvrings of a mouse for instance are unlikely to be suitable in the field. These technical requirements have all been met and there are such mobile systems available, and their big advantage is the avoidance of communication delays between a single control engineer and the twenty of so crews that are all independently communicating with that person. This is a major technique in improving real time accuracy of reporting of manual switching.

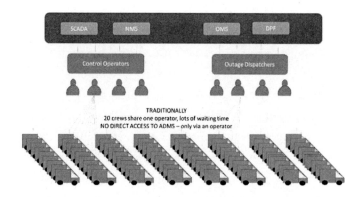

Figure 6: Crew Communication BEFORE Mobile Deployment

Mobile also can be designed to enable the crews to follow a best practice routine, to assist in risk management of their situation in the field, and to provide them with the benefits of access to the central databases for network information. The issue and completion of work over mobile is also massively more efficient than practises required prior to the availability of mobile.

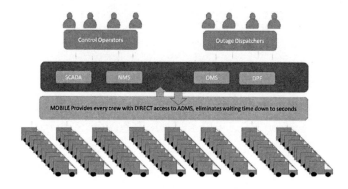

Figure 7: Crew Communication AFTER Mobile Deployment

3.6 On Line Network Analysis

The management of the electrical load being distributed to customers, is necessary to ensure no component in the distribution network becomes overloaded, and that the associated voltage available at the customer terminals is sufficient and within legal limits. Overloading means that, for instance, a cable is attempting to carry more current than it is comfortable doing, and this 'discomfort' is manifested as heat. As soon as any current begins to flow, heating will occur according to the 'I squared R' formula. I is the current measured in amps and R is the resistance present in the conducting material of the cable (usually copper or aluminium). As the current increases the heating effect increases rapidly (as the square of the current, so if the current increases threefold the heating effect increases nine-fold). This is fine provided the cable can dissipate that heat faster than it is created. It is, therefore, important to understand what type of material is in contact with the cable underground because it can help or hinder the dissipation of heat. For instance cables laid in pipes or ducting systems do not have direct contact with the mass of earth and have to be 'de-rated' by 20% recognising that air does not dissipate the heat as well as solid contact with the mass of earth. Cables, therefore, are continually warming up and cooling again dependent on how much current is passing through them. Once the rate of heating exceeds the rate of cooling, the cable is put into an unstable thermal runaway situation until the heat is sufficient to start burning the insulation layers around it. Burning creates carbon which does conduct electricity and eventually allows the current to find a conductive path through the insulation and dissipate itself in a minor or major explosion as it contacts the general mass of earth. This causes an extremely high current to flow which protection devices will detect and trip off the supply to the cable. Overloads shorten the useful life of cables. When operated within their limits, cables can last over 80 years, but regular overloading can half that over time and major overloading can of course cause immediate destruction of the asset irrespective of its age. An electricity distribution company is essentially an asset management company, investing in electrical distribution assets such as cables overhead line, transformers and switches. It is in their interest to keep these assets working, delivering energy and creating a stream of income from customers paying their bills. Allowing these assets to be damaged by misusing them, allowing them to continue operating in overload situations is bad for business, therefore, systems that monitor or calculate loading become very important. SCADA monitors those points at which communications and RTUs are installed but they cannot monitor every part of the network. Particularly since renewable generation has been embedded within the distribution networks, utilities can no longer depend on an assumption that current monitored by SCADA at source will gradually diminish towards zero as it reaches the last customer. Embedded generation can reverse current flows and smaller more remote cables can become overloaded due to local generation conditions. Embedded generation also upsets voltage drop calculations and also fault level calculations. A new all-seeing approach was needed for load management, rather than one which monitors the source and assumes everything further along the network will be less extreme, this is no longer the case.

Also when a fault does occur, for any random reason, the control engineers are seeking an alternative way to supply the customers. They need to be able to work out if this abnormal way of supplying these customers will cause an overload on the temporary donor circuit they intend to use. It is this type of decision which is one of the major causes of assets becoming overloaded. Essentially, the need to restore supplies to customers is balanced against the long-term risk to the health of the assets. The customer need is here and now, immediate, the potential damage to the asset may be years off and, therefore, it is tempting to meet the pressing need. In fact control engineers need to be supported in taking decisions that recognise both criteria. While restoring all customers might overload and damage the cable, possibly restoring supplies to 60% of customers does not overload the assets, so the correct decision might be to leave the final restoration of the 40% of customers until after the repair is complete. The control engineer has an asset management boss who would praise his decision but may also have a corporate executive who sees needless extra customer minutes lost causing the company to miss its CML target for the year and cost the company millions in fines. It is, therefore, a corporate task to examine the near immediate 'reward' for meeting CML targets, and balance that against the longer-term millions needed to replace assets earlier in their lifecycle than should have been necessary. In practice, the customer nearly always win out, and it is only overloads which will exacerbate the situation by causing immediate permanent loss of the asset, or tripping off more protection systems expanding the loss of supply to more customers, which are avoided.

To help inform these tricky decisions, it became essential that more visibility of loading and voltage conditions and fault levels could be provided. Two methods were available:

- Deploy more SCADA at enormous cost
- Invent an on-line network analysis tool for the direct real time use of operators

In fact, the solution arrived at is a bit of both. The incentives made available to meet and exceed network performance targets, provided the investment to install more SCADA monitored and controlled points on the network. These extra measurement points provide more reliable reference points for the calculations to interpolate in between.

On Line Network Analysis provides an unbalanced load flow calculation and a short circuit calculation to ascertain performance during faults.

Traditionally network analysis was a network designer's tool and the designer would initially model the network they were designing and run load flow tests and short circuit analysis over that model to ascertain its behaviour under load and fault conditions. This was all done from a 'network normal' configuration. In the DMS operational environment, control engineers are hampered in understanding load flows by the relatively small number of SCADA measurement points on the MV network. These points were all at the source ends of MV feeders providing no information regarding the voltage conditions further along the feeder or at the extreme ends of distribution networks. Control engineers relied upon the original design being robust enough to handle all operational combinations. Control engineers used their experience and their historical records to anticipate loading problems around their network. This all began to unravel with the introduction of embedded renewable generation which upset the historical monodirectional load flow patterns and in some cases reversed power flow directions. This produced a requirement for more SCADA monitored points which is an expensive and time consuming option, or for an alternative methodology to calculate the loads and voltages based on load profiles of usage per secondary transformer. Most utilities in this predicament undertook a bit of both actions. Additional SCADA points were made economic by the introduction of intelligent automation, and by using the OMS data of numbers and types of customers per secondary transformer, then load profiles could be prepared with some degree of accuracy. (This accuracy is set to improve dramatically with the introduction of smart meters, provided the utilities can gain access to the consumption data from every meter.) For higher voltage networks and for design purposes, the concept of a balanced load across three phases enabled the use of calculations which assumed all three phases to be balanced. However, operationally, further down the network, MV and LV, there are fewer customers to justify the assumption of balanced load and there are single phase spurs etc. which distort assumptions of balance. Therefore, particularly at MV and below, it is essential that the calculations of load assume unbalanced conditions and, therefore, the on-line network analysis requires a different calculation tool from that used at EHV and in the design office.

3.6.1 Load Profiles

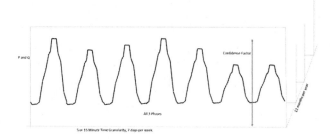

Figure 8: Typical Secondary Transformer Load Profile

When undertaking analysis of the MV network, the secondary transformers are deemed to be load points. The only measured data from the secondary substation is from a manually read maximum demand meter. This has two pointers, one activated by the load that is flowing, the other is a slave pushed by the active pointer. The slave is, therefore, left at the maximum reading the active pointer ever reached since its last reset. This data is collected approximately monthly by hand during substation inspections. The max demand figure is helpful in placing the highest point on that curve. The load at each transformer is compiled as a weekly profile with a granularity of 5 or 15 minutes between points. The data includes P and Q and covers all three phases individually. These profiles include one for every month of the year. Finally, because the data is normally estimated from the number and type of customers connected, there is a confidence factor. Some data may be accurate, taken from meter readings, but other data is estimated. It is useful to be able to identify those transformer where estimates might be suspect so that when there is corroborating evidence of what the figure should be (such as a SCADA measurement), then the calculated answer can be massaged by the confidence factors on all the transformers involved so that accurate data is protected as accurate, and the error passed between those transformers where the profile is less sure as defined by its lower confidence factor. Load data estimated from statistical examination of customers consumption has been used by energy companies for years to estimate customer bills, there is a lot of data available to make the profile useably accurate. However, the load profiles do need to be maintained, refreshed from recent evidence as and when it becomes available. The network connectivity model is the other source of data and again a focus on updating switching actions in near real time will keep the model as accurate as possible. Calculating voltage drop and fault currents depends on a knowledge of the impedance of each component in the network, and impedance is normally stored as an attribute of each component within the database. The network comprises thousands of components and if one piece of impedance data is missing then, unless other steps are taken, the calculation will fail to converge. However, this is an area where intelligent guesswork can enable a result to be achieved with minimal error. For instance there are three main sizes of MV cable in use for the last 30 years, 300sqmm, 185sqmm and 95sqmm. Historically there are a lot more but if in the absence of data the guess is made at the midsize, the error is halved if a 300 size were used when a 95 size should have been used, and vice versa. Each component, where the impedance data field is blank, is populated with a default value so that the calculation will complete and resolve to an answer. There is a calculation report which will include a note of how many default values have been used and identify them. By using a data maintenance team, using the technique of constraining the calculation to agree with known SCADA values, and using the concept of default values, this real time load flow calculation has been proven in operation to deliver results that are as accurate as SCADA measurements (95%). The data model however, does have to be commission tested, and then maintained for this accuracy to be maintained. A major improvement is approaching when there is a higher concentration of smart meters sending in 15 minute demand data, every 24 hours one day later.

3.6.2 The Effect of Embedded Renewable Energy on Distribution Networks

Designers planned for a monodirectional load flow from primary source flowing out along feeders to customer consumption points. SCADA monitoring data was stored historically so control engineers could have some idea of what to expect per season on any part of their network. Control engineers depended upon experience and learning from events, to identify tricky times to attempt switching such as closing normally open points and over time there was annotation added to the network model warning of the presence of difficult parallels etc. Renewable energy in the form of solar and wind powered generation introduced uncontrolled microgeneration into LV and MV networks. Utilities were inundated with requests for connection of additional renewable energy generation sites and this had consequences that had to be managed if the network was to remain stable. When there is sufficient local generation to export back into the network this upsets the monodirectional load flow assumptions from the original design of the network. This also could have the capability of upsetting on line transformer tap changers at Primary sites if the reverse generation grew that large, tap changers were not designed for reverse power flow operation.

SCADA measurement at the source of a feeder, or indeed on the loads of primary transformers no longer measure the total demand from customers, they only measure the nett demand which is the total demand minus that demand satisfied by embedded renewable generation downstream of the SCADA measurement point.

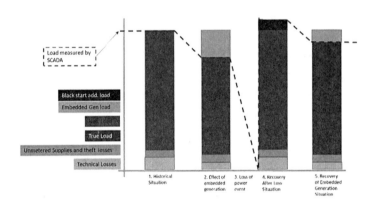

Figure 9: The Effect of Embedded Generation on Measured Load

Situation one is the historical position where the total load was supplied via the source feeder and this includes some technical losses based on the current and the length and impedance of the cables, some unmetered loads and 'non-technical' losses caused by theft, and the total demand of the customers connected to the feeder.

Situation two shows the effect of the presence of some embedded generation. Embedded generation removes some of the network losses because the demand is satisfied by generation close to the point of use, therefore, avoiding causing loss on the feeder supplying the premises. Unmetered supplies and theft will still be connected, and it is possible that all or some of this demand is met by overspill where embedded generation exceeds the demand from the premises hosting the generation. The SCADA measurement only sees and measures the Nett load, and cannot 'see' the load satisfied by embedded generation, unless that embedded generation is sufficiently large to merit SCADA monitoring. If nothing else was known, SCADA would be telling control engineers that the load has been dropping because it cannot see the embedded generation satisfying a proportion of local demand.

Situation three envisages a loss of supply due to a fault occurring. SCADA registers zero load, and embedded generation will also either trip due to the fault or if it cannot support 'ride-through', it will stop generating. Let us say the fault is repaired and all the previous customers are again going to be re-supplied from the original source.

Situation four shows the reconnection of supply. The control engineer knows the SCADA was registering say 100 Amps before the trip, but on resupply has to pick up the nett load, plus the embedded generation contribution, plus the 'black start' additional load caused by loss of diversity. The 'surprise load' is not the black start, that has been a well-known element of resupply after failure for many years. The

45

surprise is the amount of compensation needed to replace embedded generation which might be totally different day to day as the weather conditions support more or less renewable generation.

Situation five shows the embedded generation being re-established and making the SCADA reading look like demand is reducing, whereas in fact demand has stayed the same but is being increasingly met by local embedded generation again. The fault may have lasted from a full daylight afternoon into early evening when embedded solar generation is reducing, therefore, the amount of embedded generation is different from the amount that was lost a few hours previously. Wind power contribution too will alter as the winds change.

Historical data did not collect associated weather-related data, therefore, the presence of winds and variations in insolation did not relate to the demand figures at the time. However, as embedded generation increased to noticeable levels, this had the effect of deflating the demand from the traditional source at the Primary substation and above that at the grid supply point. Newly added loading data to historical databases requires to include knowledge of conditions and their estimates of locally generated units from wind and solar installations.

With additional sources of generation, then fault levels voltage levels altered along feeders leading to situations where violations of standards and limits became possible.

Similarly, loading conditions could infringe capacity limits on parts of the network if a sufficient combination of renewable generators were active.

This disruption upset control engineer's traditional ways of estimating loads and conditions at paralleling points, but it also depressed actual load as seen by the transmission network.

The Transmission Control Room Energy Management System (EMS), usually operates with a set of contingency plans but if the 'as seen' demand is lower than the actual demand, due to some load being satisfied from local generation, then the contingency plans at EMS level are operating on unrealistically low loads. The brown start or black start conditions would be significantly worse than the historical loading data at bulk supply points because all the local generation will have also switched off and the restoration from grid would have to include an extra element of load relating to that serviced from local generation.

These effects raised the business case for more knowledge of loading, voltage and fault level conditions throughout the distribution networks, and supported extensions of SCADA and the need for on line load flow and fault level calculations.

3.7 DPF (Distribution Power Flow) Load Flow Calculation

On line load flow uses the on line live operational network model to analyse the currents flowing through every section of the network and the voltage levels at every secondary substation busbar. These calculations are based in part on any measured data available, and on load profiles created for every secondary transformer. Since it can also display power and reactive power it is often referred to as DPF, Distribution Power Flow. DPF has been deployed on MV networks for over 15 years, and it can operate in response to a question posed by the control engineer, "What if I close this switch?" The DPF (Distribution Power Flow) function will assume the switch has been moved to its new position and analyse the network with its proposed connectivity and produce a set of answers of voltage, current, power, reactive power per phase for every cable and overhead line section and every secondary substation transformer MV busbar. The results can be provided in a summary screen and overlaid over the network diagram model, with potential violations highlighted in different colours. The calculations can be invoked in 'study mode' during the preparation of planned outages to ascertain if proposed switching actions cause limit violations during the switching or in the temporary abnormal state created so that work can commence. Finally, there is a continually operating mode, where the calculations are continually running in the background and resolve answers every four minutes or so. This creates massive amounts of data per component and this can be shown on the operational network model or made available via a menu or hover mouse function including a mini trending graph showing recent variations with a comparison to previous day. The data can be stored in the real time database, it can be used for calculations, presented visually on the network diagram, and it can be configured to have the same types of limits and alarm generation just as true SCADA generated points can. Finally this calculated data can be stored, however, traditional historian databases are structured on a cost per point and become uneconomic when the millions of points now being stored every four minutes become available. A modern cloud computing environment has been created to accommodate massive time series data storage to hold this data.

Online load flow has enabled a step increase in visibility of distribution network loads and voltage levels and this is timely functionality, stepping in just in time as the old historical data and estimation methods begin to fail due to the changing nature of the use made of distribution networks to host embedded generation.

3.8 Fault Level Calculation SCC (Short Circuit Calculation)

Fault level is an assessment of the amount of current that will flow when a fault occurs. The software allows the type of fault to be set and the position of fault to be set for specific calculations but in practice the fault location is not known in advance and the type of fault is not known, therefore, SCC operates on a worst case set of assumptions and tests it against faults located anywhere on the network. The function then stores the worst answers for each component and lists or displays them as required.

3.9 DTF

DTF is Distribution Transfer Function. Control engineers are forever making choices of how to transfer load from one source to another, and they use the 'normally open' points within their networks to effect these transfers. Traditionally control engineers would do a quick mental sum of the circuit capacity minus the load to ascertain how much 'spare' capacity was available. DTF is the software function that provides that quick assessment of current (only) to assist in switching decisions that need a near immediate answer. Obviously a full 'what if' load flow could also be done but when under time constraints (intelligent automation attempting to restore customers within three minutes), then minimising delay becomes important.

3.10 FDIR Fault Detection, Isolation & Restoration

For many years, engineers have used automatic restoration as a means of quickly restoring supplies to rural communities. There are risks involved in doing this due to the absence of any on site information at the locus of the fault. However, 70% of rural overhead line trips are transient and, therefore, justified the use of auto-reclosers, to produce 'dumb automation'. With the advent of DMS, the system has access simultaneously to all the data being updated by all the control engineers and all the incoming data from crews via mobile, SCADA and call centre. It became possible to design more intricate intelligent automation schemes and apply them generically across MV distribution networks to make automated restoration a much more available solution.

FDIR, Fault Detection Isolation and Restoration is a function that draws on integrating capabilities from SCADA, on line analysis and switching management in NMS to respond automatically to a fault occurrence. There are several methodologies used by the various ADMS vendors to achieve similar objectives. Some use a "ladder logic" approach similar to the traditional substation automation approach, but drive it from ADMS so at least the other ADMS functions are aware of the changes to the network. This remains relatively inflexible in that it cannot operate on anything but a pre-set network configuration. A step forward is a scripted approach with several different scripts available to be applied to several different commonly found distribution network configurations. This enables the script to be tested once but then deployed on as many feeders that fit that particular configuration. Both methods suffer from some underlying weaknesses. The maintenance workload they incur increases in proportion to the number of feeders covered by FDIR, increasing costs when the utility is under pressure to contain and reduce costs. Secondly, the risks of automation are such that many utilities insist on a manual review before authorising an automated restoration to proceed. The most refined implementations of FDIR functions remove the need for manual authorisation checks, can be applied over a variety of network configurations and consequently have reduced the relationship between scalability and increasing maintenance costs. The business case for FDIR is that 50% or 66% of customers are restored in under three minutes and most regulators allow that to be defined as a momentary outage and therefore does not count towards the reliability statistics of frequency and duration of outages. When FDIR runs out of options for an automated restoration it will stop and then the control engineer can assess what has been done and assess how the faulted section can be further minimised in scope and size by manual switching. FDIR can make recommendations for the proposed switching actions to finally isolate the smallest fault section. FDIR switching actions will be captured in a fault switching log within NMS and customer restoration stages automatically captured into an OMS fault log. This manual fault investigation is still necessary but is now only a half or a third of its original complexity and size.

3.11 ANM

ANM, Active Network Management is a function which has become necessary with the advent of embedded renewable energy generation with distribution networks. The MV network has historically been passive, taking energy from a known set of sources and flowing that mono-directionally along feeders to the points of consumption on customer sites. This being the case the design of networks could allow tapering of feeders from large cross section near the source to smaller cross sections as the feeder extends towards the last few customer connections. This is the network state inherited by all utilities, but they now face the problem of multi directional power flows and embedded generation. This upsets the voltage levels, the fault levels and the current flows and makes the availability of reactive power a novel consideration within distribution networks. These network constraints require constant monitoring once embedded generation is connected, and this, for the massive HV and MV network requires a more dedicated function operating in localised areas of the network monitoring specific constraints. This is achieved within DMS by integrating aspects of the traditional SCADA alarm view DMS switching and intelligent automation. The constraint is defined as a set of limits on the assets at risk. These constraints when hit, raise an alarm but also set in motion the ANM functions. These functions can interact with embedded generation to level off generation, reduce it, or stop it altogether and has an embedded logic that respects the various connection contracts of each generator. As the constraint is removed ANM then restores the generation to optimise the use of embedded generation.

3.12 IVVC

IVVC is Integrated Volt Var Control, which is necessary in some locations where there are very long feeders and uses strategically placed capacitor banks to boost voltage levels along feeder to keep the remote end voltage within legal limits. This intelligent function monitors voltages and losses along a feeder and can be set to minimise reactive losses or maintain voltage within limits, by interacting with capacitor banks connected to the SCADA system.

3.13 Reports

Utilities require a lot of data from the operational experience of their networks. The DMS is uniquely situated to capture that data, in switching logs, outage logs and from the measured and calculated loading of the network. Fault reporting is a specialist area of reporting which requires to be accurate in real time, and available throughout the organisation in real time, and available to social media utility web sites which inform the public at large about the current state of supply within the region. Reporting accuracy drives a discipline through switching management and outage management to attempt to keep the systems updated as close to real time as is practicable. In UK for instance, the utilities can be fined if their outage reporting fails an accuracy audit and this does affect their risk/reward analysis for supply reliability. Where systems or processes are insufficient to keep up with real time accuracy, then the utilities are involved in expensive historical investigation and correction prior to reporting their results. This is obviously duplicated effort and the reports themselves are less useful because they are not available on time to inform strategic real time decisions. Techniques to improve real time accuracy will be discussed in a later section of the book. However, the DMS now holds much more data that is of interest to the utility, it has counters on every switch, manual or SCADA controlled, to monitor the usage and, therefore, highlight switches that need maintained. All the network loading data and voltage level data is of interest in assessing voltage control requirements and network constraints. This of course is available from SCADA for the limited points connected, but with the addition of on line analysis, this provides saturated coverage of the complete MV network. Finally every outage also has a fault report which can hold data relating to cause and the actual faulted component, and these reports are very useful in strategic assessment of network performance in identifying areas of network which need reinforcement or refurbishment. The operational environment, however, is a secure area both physically and from an IT security standpoint. Reporting, therefore, requires techniques to extract the data from the secure environment and make it available on the outside of the operational firewall. This can be achieved using the 'positive pressure' principle which allows a 'leak' out of the system through a specific port but blocks any inflow to the system via that port. The reporting database receives its input from the main DMS servers, but all enquiries for reports hit a proxy server for verification and then obtain the answers from the reporting environment and not the operational environment.

4

Data Storage in ADMS

ADMS contains data of several different types and, therefore, requires different types of storage medium to be available.

4.1 RDBMS

The RDBMS is the Relational Database Management System, and the most prevalent one is provided by Oracle. RDBMS is used to permanently hold the network asset and normal connectivity data. To avoid duplicating data and master databases, RDBMS can obtain its asset data from the asset management master DB over an interface. This is usually done when the ADMS is being set up and thereafter the interface requires to manage incremental changes. The definition of which data is needed within the DMS is based on what is operationally necessary for control engineers to function effectively on a 24 x 7 x 365 basis in real time. This makes it imperative to hold that subset of asset data within the DMS operations environment, which is specially designed to operate continuously and securely. There is also additional data not held in Asset Management systems, but is necessary for asset operations, and this includes the detailed design of operational interlocks on switches and the detailed voltage and current monitoring and measurement points that are connected to SCADA. There are masses of configuration items within the DMS that are of little or no interest to Asset management master DB (such as the set points of alarms) and, therefore, these data subsets are mastered within DMS.

One particular aspect of RDBMS is the storage of the current state, rather than the designed normal state of the network. This, of necessity, is mastered in DMS because DMS is the first and only system that can obtain that data in real time either via SCADA or via onsite crew updates.

A major function of the RDBMS is its role in creating back up files, usually on a daily basis. A related function is when introducing a server into the DMS environment, the RDBMS will populate the server with the default settings and switch positions as taken at the most recent backup.

The 24 x 7 x 365 availability requirement introduces the need for multiple synchronised versions of the RDBMS and the DMS provides functions to enable and maintain that.

4.2 RTDB

The RTDB is the Real Time Database, used by SCADA to import and refresh data extracted from the RTUs in the remote substations. RT holds all this measured data and the digital signal of on/off switching states etc. and in concept it is similar to a spreadsheet, with a cell dedicated to each point. As these points are scanned by SCADA the data overwrites each cell accordingly. RT has functions that enable it to manufacture calculated values from the measured values that might be power from voltage and current measurements, or averages etc. Each point also has configuration options enabling decisions to be made such as making this value visible in a designated location on the network diagram model, and sending this real time data into a historical archive. RTDB is also used to hold points generated from on line load flow calculations.

4.3 Historian Real Time Data Store

The Historian or RTDS, has the function of capturing real time data and instead or over writing it in a single 'cell' RTDS stacks data in columns, therefore, enabling access to historical trends and trending graphs. To reduce the volume stored this data can be concentrated into half hour averages etc.

This data can be made available back onto the DMS operational network model or driven out into a reporting environment.

4.4 Reports DB

The Reporting DB is the mechanism for extracting the data from the operationally secure environment and making it available for the creation of corporate reports. The reporting DB is usually much bigger than the DMS RDBMS because it also acts as the archive DB. Some corporate reports require historical data as well as current data. On top of the DB function, report writing tools enable standard reports and special reports to be created. The mechanism for populating the reporting environment should ideally allow access to data in 'near real time' so that real time reports are available to management without the need to interrupt operations with questions concerning the current network state. Near real time data is used to assess strategies during extended storms and to inform regulatory bodies and the public of electricity supply losses and restoration times. The DMS is a rich source of network condition intelligence and the most effective electricity utilities maximise the use of this data within asset management strategy as well as in assessing network reliability.

5

The Interaction of DMS with Other Corporate IT Systems

The DMS primarily acts as a tool for the operation of the network in real time. This needs to be secure and 24 x 7 x 365 reliable, available and capable of real time performance, but should not be an islanded system. If data duplications and double work are to be eliminated, then DMS must exist and interact with the other major corporate systems. Most business process to business process interfaces can use standard technology the SOAP/XML. The Simple Object Access Protocol is a messaging protocol for exchanging structured information between IT systems. XML the Extensible Mark-up Language, allows clients to invoke services and receive responses from independent platforms used by other corporate systems.

5.1 EMS

EMS, Energy Management System, is the transmission control room IT system. Many DMS started life as a development evolved from EMS bringing their functions down to HV and MV. However, DMS has staked its own claim as a different product due to several major differences:

The EMS controls a relatively small network in which every circuit is highly important.

The DMS controls a relatively huge network in which each circuit is relatively unimportant.

THE EMS has a focus on maintaining a generation/load balance and the maintenance of a stable frequency in the energy network.

The DMS has directly connected customers and its focus is on delivering reliable supply to customers.

The EMS network diagram changes infrequently and can be supported by a manual process.

The DMS network diagram changes continuously and needs a dedicated business process automated within the DMS functions.

The EMS has 100% coverage to open close switches anywhere on its network.

The DMS has only 20% coverage representing the primary SS switches and a few outlying switches on the MV network to enable intelligent automation.

The EMS is totally operated as an active network and needs specific functions to identify risks and constraints the focus being on avoiding loss.

The DMS is still mainly a passive network, with emerging active elements, and its major focus is still reactive, responding to losses rather than anticipating and avoiding them.

The SCADA function is present in both EMS and DMS, however, the DMS requires a massive point count compared to EMS, therefore, justifying a separate SCADA system.

The relative importance of EMS would outrank the needs of DMS if there were an IT system failure, however, DMS with its direct relationship to customer supplies has sufficient business case to merit its own priority as an IT system.

The interface between EMS and DMS is relatively simple and easily defined. The change of network ownership occurs within a few Bulk Supply Points. There is a standard protocol, ICCP (Inter Control Centre Protocol) which enables data from EMS to be also present in DMS, and, therefore, the DMS can be updated at its source points with voltage levels, currents and fault levels from the source EMS points. Interfaces are always a source of error and maintenance, therefore, their presence is only to be tolerated when they are imperative. The size of the interface, the number of SCADA points being cross referred between the systems, can be minimised to the incoming grid transformer circuit breakers and bus section switches only. Many RTUs are dual ported enabling them to report to two different SCADA systems.

5.2 CRM

CRM, Customer Relationship Management, is usually the master of customer data, names, addresses, and telephone numbers. Within the DMS, the OMS function needs access to a subset of that data and again, it requires 24 x 7 x 365 availability and reliability and operate in real time. An interface into the DMS RDBMS will store the slave copy of the customer data subset sufficient for OMS purposes. Initially this interface would populate the DMS, and thereafter the interface would support incremental updates from the master CRM database. The DMS requires to add operational data to these records, by adding the point of supply information, LV feeder and secondary transformer.

OMS and CRM also interact on telephone calls to and from customers in relation to outages. This can either be the regular CRM call taking function interfacing into the OMS or it can be an OMS dedicated call taking application co-hosted within the CRM Call centre call taking system. The nature of no supply call recording, is one of feast and famine. On average there may be only one call every two minutes throughout the year, but the average is meaningless because faults are random and storms are random but have the effect of concentrating many calls into very short timescales. This variable workload is disruptive to the normal work of CRM Call centres which is why some OMS also supply their own Call taking application over a web infrastructure which can be ramped up fast when emergencies occur using staff temporarily re-allocated from their normal day job.

The call taking interface can operate bi directionally with OMS keeping the Call centre up to date with recent changes in customers off supply, progress reports per outage and restorations of supply. The Call taking interface is now a standard product available for most OMSs. Both aspects of interface to CRM are supported with SOAP/XML interfaces.

5.3 GIS

GIS Geospatial Information System is the organisation of electricity distribution assets based on their geolocation. As such GIS lays claim to be the master of the network diagram and the DMS network diagram can start life as an import from GIS. Modern GIS installations will support CIM/GML (Common Information Model, Geospatial Mark-up Language) as the basis for the interface. Again the major use of the interface, after first installation, is for incremental updates of the many changes undertaken on the HV and MV networks. There are troublesome issues in the relationship between GIS and DMS in that DMS has multiple uses of network diagrams for SCADA/switching management/outage management and network analysis. GIS is unlikely to hold all the data needed for a DMS diagram. GIS is not updated in real time, therefore, although GIS is a master of the network diagram, it is the as planned/as installed system NORMAL version which GIS masters. The current state of connectivity is unavoidably mastered within the DMS. SCADA data will probably be originally obtained from a legacy SCADA system which would have had its own representation of the network. Switching management is most clearly illustrated on a schematic diagram rather than a geospatial diagram and modern DMS provide both. The GIS may or may not support both geospatial and schematic and where it does support schematic it may not follow the preferred representation of the schematic required by operational needs. There are several issues with an insistence that GIS is master of the electricity network model:

Accuracy in GIS is accuracy of location, whereas accuracy in DMS is twofold, accurate connectivity and accuracy in timeous update as close to real time as possible.

Responsibility for DMS accuracy, rests with the control engineers and or senior authorised field engineers who are, in extremis, legally responsible if errors lead to accidents or fatalities. Therefore, DMS staff are always going to review, correct where necessary, and approve, any update provided by GIS.

The connectivity accuracy issue is particularly relevant in congested urban areas where several cables are in close proximity with many cross over situations. GIS cannot, on its own, decipher when cables cross or when they connect. Experience of several implementations of DMS, where the GIS was believed to be of good quality data and used as source data, found that during the process of testing and commissioning, multiple connectivity errors were identified, on every implementation, no exception. This being the case, GIS should defer to DMS to obtain connectivity in congested areas.

The incremental update procedures put in place to keep DMS and GIS synchronised, must recognise that GIS is not a real time system but DMS is. GIS can handle future versions of the network as new designs are planned in advance, but the actual update to confirm that design has been installed and connected will sit in a queue of updates that the GIS data updating team continuously work through. Some GIS have update backlogs kept within a week, most are within a month and some are three to six months behind in their updates. DMS in contrast requires a real time update. For instance, a new secondary substation (consisting of a transformer and ring main switching unit and an LV distribution board) needs to be connected into the live network model within seconds of confirmation from site that the connections are complete. The reasons for this are simple, the next operational tasks that the control engineer and site crew have to agree on is how and where to test the new installation. The control engineer needs their control room model to duplicate what the crews are facing on site or misunderstandings can occur and mistakes made. This incremental updating process does exist in some vendors ADMSs and it solves the timing issues by informing the DMS of the planned version in advance of the installation being ready to connect. This 'patch' to the network diagram is sent over the CIM/GML interface and stored by the DMS in its file of future patches to be installed. As the control engineers check and authorise the planned outage switching, they also review and check the patch change for the network diagram model. The as built version is agreed between the commissioning engineers and control and the diagram update is prepared and approved for use in advance along with the switching plan for the outage. In this way, both requirements are met, the GIS as the master of the normal state, provides the update, and enables the DMS to install it in real time as master of current connectivity. This interface posts incremental changes from GIS to DMS but in fact it should be a two way interface enabling DMS to inform GIS of the final connection.

5.4 AMS

The AMS, Asset Management System, may be the GIS or a dedicated asset application. A SOAP/XML interface enables DMS to obtain the necessary attributes for each operational component, and in turn, an interface or reports will pass back to Asset Management the data on reliability, fault root cause analyses, network loadings and voltage levels, to inform new design and reinforcement decisions and maintenance planning.

5.5 SMMS

The Smart Meter Management System interface can provide two main types of information to the DMS. The SMI can supplant customer call information in notification of outages and restoration. The issue here is large outages may simultaneously affect thousands of smart meters and these 'no supply' messages will exceed the communications bandwidth and backlog. Meanwhile, the DMS intelligent automation will restore supply to hundreds of customers within three minutes and these meters will be attempting to send 'supply restored' messages adding to the confusion and backlog of messages. This interface process, therefore, requires to be managed in a way that avoids mass simultaneous messaging. For outages that trip a SCADA device, the DMS will know of the outage just as the first messages appear in the SMMS master from their meters. DMS can re-apply the OMS interface to CRM, directing it to the SMMS master server and it can be used as a trigger to specific ping requests to a sample of meters to verify the outage scope. SMMS can return the response to DMS confirming the outage. For outages discovered by customer call cluster analysis, DMS can either ping specific meters directly or make a ping request to SMMS over the interface.

The second area of the SMMS interface is in providing loading data to populate the load profile of each secondary transformer. SMMS collects all the meter readings every 15 minutes and passes them to the SMMS master within 24 hours. DMS holds the connectivity of the network and can, therefore, advise the SMMS on which meter readings to add together to obtain an LV feeder load and secondary substations loads. SMI should undertake the collection of this data into a load profile and pass it over the interface to DMS. DMS should handle this data as a background updating process improving its load profile estimates based on actual SMMS data but one day removed. DMS on line network analysis depends on these load profiles but recognises they currently include estimates. The accuracy of the estimates is reflected in a confidence factor, and the SMMS interface data should provide a step change improvement in these confidence factors, enabling DPF to be as accurate as SCADA. This interface has the advantage that the meter data is grouped on the basis of connectivity that the DMS is keeping accurate in real time. This interface, therefore, will identify abnormal connectivity and automatically provide the answer for the odd high or low readings that would otherwise require verification by manual investigation to ascertain why they differ from the norm of the profile. This is a useful feature in itself because it provides evidence that will verify or challenge DTF spare capacity calculations. Using the interface in this way also ensures compliance with data protection legislation anonymising individual meter readings into summated load profiles.

5.6 Embedded Renewable Generation

The presence of domestic solar panel roof installations will distort demand assessment unless every such installation has import export metering capability reported into the SMMS. Similarly wind generation connected directly into the MV or HV network will mask the true load from the SCADA measurements at the source of the feeder. DMS can handle these variables provided sample data can be captured and stored. One way to achieve this is to install solar panels and a weather station at every Primary substation and make the assumption that levels of insolation etc. at the primary also apply to the secondary substations around it and to the domestic premises known to have solar panels. Customer data in DMS can have extra attributes added to it identifying the number of panels and orientation factors compared to the sample panels at the primary SS. The weather station wind speed and direction data can be applied to the capacity of known wind turbines in the vicinity to estimate their contribution to demand.

6

Maintenance of DMS

Utilities don't think twice about the need for maintenance of their major transformers, substations and switches, this is because electrical power engineering is their area of expertise. Computing systems are a different speciality, and the power engineering departments fondly think that IT is being looked after by their IT department, not their problem. In fact there are data update aspects within ADMS maintenance that can impact on overall operational network performance and, therefore, should not be delegated to other departments where these impacts are not obvious.

- Operational Maintenance of the network data within the running system:

o SCADA Updates: monitoring and refreshing some 200,000 points in seconds.
o SCADA Point Data Updates: adding FDIR introduces new RTUs and additional points on a near daily basis.

- Switching Management: Connectivity data – 100,000 switching items changing connectivity either temporarily or permanently every year.
- Customer Premises Connectivity Data: on the basis of one million customers and a growth rate of 2% implies 20,000 updates per year.
- OMS Call Answering: an annual average of a call per two minutes being ramped up to 4,000 calls an hour in a storm.
- OMS progress data tracking the investigation and restoration of 20,000 faults per year.
- Network Asset Data Attributes – millions of attributes updating say 5% per year.
- Network Analysis: the presentation of calculation results.
- Network Model Updates: graphical data in the form of network diagram model(s) – 2,000 patches updated per year, per network model, at MV.

- Generic IT systems maintenance

Every IT system has the generic components:

- Server and client workstation hardware – typical lifespan five to ten years.
- IT operating systems such as UNIX, Linux, MS Windows, iOS etc, typically support versions up to three years old.
- Third party software used for the databases and IT security packages typically up to three years for

databases, but security systems drip feed upgrades as threats evolve.

o The application software will have a product version, and there will be a support contract for correction of bugs.

o Application software: product version upgrades to gain access to new functions. This may be available as a maintenance function version upgrade (if the software is rigorously productised to start with) or alternatively, access to new functions is gained via another major IT project typically every seven years.

6.1 Operational Updates of the Network Data

This data is being continuously updated during the operation of the ADMS. Logging switching actions, updating OMS incidents, adding new substations or equipment to the network, etc. The maintenance strategy can and does have a direct impact on the ability of ADMS to drive network performance improvement. In a real time system like DMS, network data is subject to two major sources of error:

- 'TIME WARP' errors where there is a significant time difference between a connectivity change occurring on site and the representation of that change becoming visible and apparent to the ADMS and its operators.

- 'CONNECTIVITY' errors occur when the ADMS network model connectivity is different from the actual network connectivity.

6.1.1 Time Warp Errors

Time warp errors are introduced by the business processes in use in the utility, some of which are prone to introducing delay in updates, particularly at times of high activity. It is during the times of high activity that the DMS must perform optimally, and performance degradations that increase as volumes of data increase must be identified and eliminated or reduced.

SCADA systems update the real time database and the network diagram in seconds. Occasionally an increase in the flow of data, for instance during a storm, or a problem with the communication network or its components can upset this regime and the data will be automatically flagged as 'old' and, therefore, suspect. SCADA systems already include many strategies to mitigate response problems such as prioritising specific types of data and the ADMS can also help in mitigation by directing alarms only to the operators controlling each configured zone, so that operators can share out the workload.

SCADA point data is continually being added particularly when the utility adopts intelligent automation projects which will add typically three RTUs and 150 points for every circuit to which FDIR is applied. Utilities have deployed FDIR on to 900 circuits at a rate of 150 circuits a year. This implies 450 RTUs and 22,500 points added to the diagram and database in a year, therefore, it is a daily update task which must occur without disruption of the live system. Modern SCADA functions embedded as an integrated function within ADMS can and do support methods of on-line introduction of new RTUs lines and points into the system.

Switching management is a process surrounded by safety procedures designed to minimise the risk of misunderstandings in the communications between control engineers and operations crews on site. Each control engineer 'manages' approximately 20 different jobs, which implies communicating with at least 20 crews in the field. All twenty crews want to start switching early in the morning so that work can commence after the safe zone has been created by switching. Similarly, every crew wants to restore the network to normal in the late afternoon prior to finishing work for the day. The effect is to concentrate the demand for access to the control engineer into the first and last hours of the working day, and there are inevitably queues formed of crews waiting to talk with the control engineer before they can proceed to the next switching action. Both the deliberate phrases and format of the content of the messages, and the queueing, contribute to the time elapsed during each switching instruction conversation and each crew confirmation of completion. 100,000 instructions per year, plus their queue delay, each take between five and 30 minutes on a normal day and extending to possibly three hours during a high activity day such as a storm. The ADMS diagram will degrade in accuracy as the time warp errors increase, until there is a tipping point when the ADMS will lose control of the storm in real time.

Strategies such as delegating control to crews, letting them proceed inside a part of the network delegated to them alone, is one strategy commonly used during storms. The crew returns control back to the central control room after restoration is complete, but the ADMS has been out of date all the time during the delegation, and any advanced features such as load flow calculations, intelligent automation as well as real time situation reports, are all inaccurate due to the time warp errors.

In 2006, a new approach introduced a specialised Mobile application specifically designed to meet the safety procedures of switching management and this enables crews to obtain messages and send back replies directly communicating with the ADMS, circumventing the queues waiting to speak in person to the control engineer. This revolutionised the management of manual switching and improved the update response time down to seconds, for 80% of transactions. The 20% represents messages sent while the crew and its mobile were located in poor reception areas. In such cases the mobile buffers the messages and informs the sender of that fact. When the crew travel through an area of improved reception the buffer automatically flushes enabling the crew to send and receive messages caught in the buffer.

The time warp issues of switching management can, therefore, be managed by the introduction of specialised mobile functionality which respects and supports the safety issues involved in HV and MV switching. This does not apply to LV switching which is not controlled on an item by item oversight by control. This will be covered as the management of the LV network is discussed.

Time Warp Errors in Customer Connectivity Updating

Customer connections, or more rigorously customer premise connectivity to the network also requires to be maintained. This data is problematical in that there are millions of connections, and updates occur at a rate usually proportional to the rate of development of the country. So an advanced western European country saw most of its electrification in the 1950s and 60s, and today experiences only a 1 to 2% change year on year. Whereas a third world country starting out on electrification might see connections growing at 7 to 12% per year. When an ADMS or a GIS project starts up there might be a deliberate exercise to capture the connectivity of premises, but this is not a dynamic methodology, it is a photograph at one moment in time, and a customer connections update procedure is needed to handle the incremental changes year on year thereafter. Even at 2% growth this represents 20,000 customer connectivity updated per year for a one million customer utility. The second aspect of this issue is the granularity of the connection. When this data was first required for OMS to operate, then groups of customers per secondary substation was sufficiently accurate to enable a crew to be sent to the correct substation to investigate. New functions and the introduction of local micro renewable generation, now require increased granularity down to particular sections of LV cable and the individual phase connection, so that load profiles of transformers can be accurately ascertained from smart meter data.

It is true that the effect of one customer connection missing is lost in the noise when there are one million customers connected. One must, therefore, ask if this is really necessary to drive up the accuracy of this data, when the only benefit was a negligible error impact on customer minutes lost and customer interruptions. In answer there are two reasons, the first is that, uncontrolled and unmonitored, this error in updating will grow over time and eventually the error will be sufficient to interfere with the accuracy of OMS outage predictions, and this will become evident during some time of stress on the data such as during a storm.

Secondly, new functions continued to be added to ADMS and, to be effective, some of these depend on low time warp errors and the increased granularity of customer connection data. For instance, load flow calculations at MV need minimised time warp error in reporting MV switching actions. Also LV load flow calculations on networks involving embedded micro renewable generation cannot be properly understood unless per phase customer connectivity data is available. This error will increase as more generation is connected, and this effect is driving the requirement for better LV network management. This per phase data does not exist in many utilities at all.

Customer connectivity can be updated via an ADMS interface to GIS. As the customer premise services are installed, that update can be sent into the DMS database as a 'trivial' update not requiring the operations department to check or authorise its inclusion in DMS. There are several potential issues with this approach:

- The laying of a service cable does not necessarily mean it also has a meter connected nor a customer resident and, therefore, it may not be an actual customer yet.
- The plotting of the millions of service cables produces a lot of low priority updates to GIS, and these may be deferred in favour of higher priority updates, therefore, this process might introduce long delays in introducing the connection to the DMS database.

- There is the well-known issue of connectivity errors within GIS data where there is difficulty in ascertaining to which main cable the customer service cable is connected.
- Where customer connectivity data has been 'discovered' within DMS by being involved in a fault incident, then DMS may already know of the connection and the incident confirms that the connectivity is accurate. The GIS interface may overwrite this connection once it has been updated via the automated ADMS interface from GIS, and this overwrite may include an error.

There is an alternative to the graphic updates done in GIS, ADMS can have an interface directly with the CRM customer database. Within DMS, a text based list of connected premises per LV feeder and per secondary substation is held and maintained, totally separately from any graphical representation in GIS. The advantages in this approach are:

- There is definitely a meter and a customer connected if the data exists in the CRM database.
- Due to its relation to billing, there is a strong business case to keep the CRM database accurate and up to date.
- The actual decision of WHERE the connection attaches to the network is left to administration staff in each local district.
- A report identifies the addresses with no link to supply transformer and also transformers with no customer addresses linked to them.

- A fast and simple drag and drop technique can be used to associate new addresses from a text based list to the local transformer.
- This strategy takes customer connection updates and pops them straight in ADMS within 24 hours of them appearing in the CRM as new customers.
- ADMS connectivity can be proven if and when there are outages.
- There is no huge problem if a few premises connections are attached wrongly, as long as they are attached quickly. The data can be held with an accuracy flag, and only confirmed when it is proven by one method or another.

Time Warp Errors in Customer No Supply Call Taking

For many parts of the remote MV network, the primary protection device can be a fuse or circuit breaker which has no communication capability and, therefore, SCADA is unaware of their operation. In these cases it is customers calling an emergency no supply number which first notifies the control room that a fault has occurred, and the customer service business process and telephony equipment to facilitate customer call taking becomes important in identifying the scope and location of the fault. OMS call taking is affected by the number of telephone lines available, as well as the number of operators taking calls. The problem is that call centres are staffed for normal call traffic, but storms and large scale outages cause massive peaks in the number of calls received per hour. The customer service business process has to be designed to include the ability to suddenly ramp up the number of call takers and number of telephone lines so that customers do not experience an annoying delay in their call being answered.

By introducing a web based call taker application, calls can be contracted out to remote locations that use totally different telephone lines. Alternatively, if there are sufficient lines but not enough call takers, the web-based call taker application can be installed on the PCs of any office-based staff and they can quickly convert into additional call takers for the duration of the emergency. With mobile phone technology many rural customers keep the 'no supply' number for their local electricity company in their phone directory and can make a call within a few minutes having first checked that it is not merely part of their own supply that has faulted. If SCADA had been informed the ADMS would have been reacting within seconds, with a good customer service process and call taking installation calls can be passed to the OMS part of ADMS within two to five minutes, but critically it is the telephony methodology used by the utility which avoids customers from long waits to record their call.

Time Warp Errors in OMS Incident Updating

Crews responding to fault incidents face the same issue as crews attempting to confirm their switching actions, namely there are 20 crews trying to gain access to one OMS dispatcher to update their progress. The importance of reducing time warp errors is crucial in keeping the real time situation report accurate in real time because this is the source of data which influences strategic decisions by major incident managers. A second function was developed for the specialised operations Mobile application to enable OMS incidents to be dispatched to crews and enable crews to automatically update directly into the OMS incident logs as progress is made, therefore, avoiding the communications bottleneck inherent in person-to-person communications.

Time Warp Errors in Updating Network Asset Attributes

The assets modelled on the ADMS network diagram have the capability to store attributes of that asset. The ADMS deliberately does not store all the attributes of an asset, as might be held on an asset management database, but only those attributes which assist in the operational management of these assets. These can include its make and type, rating, date time and reason last operated, and, when on line network analysis was added to ADMS a whole new raft of attributes had to be added so that the calculations could access or calculate the impedance of the asset and its effect on the network around it. This type of data is mainly imported in bulk at the start of an ADMS project, however, there is a continual addition to attributes as new incremental updates are made to the model and new functions added to ADMS require more attribute data to be held. Attribute updates are mainly achieved over interfaces from the master asset system or GIS or some other host system. The issue of attribute update is vastly simplified when dealing with a fully integrated ADMS where all the ADMS functions use the same diagram and the same relational database, therefore, one update updates all functions.

Time Warp Errors in Network Analysis Updates

Prior to an on-line network analysis function being embedded in ADMS, network analysis for distribution networks was primarily a design function ensuring that networks would provide legal voltage and remain within the loading capacity limits of all network components, in the NORMAL configuration of the connected network. Trying to obtain abnormal configuration load flow results was impractical. Firstly, the design system model would have to be altered to reflect the abnormal configuration, then the calculation would be run and then the result passed back to control. This was not an adequate solution for real time situations. Online network analysis was invented to overcome operational overloading in real time circumstances particularly when the network was required to operate in an abnormal configuration.

Modern ADMS has an on-line capability to analyse the current network configuration directly on the ADMS operational network model. (Note the importance of reducing time warp error.) This can be done either on request or as a continuous background task running behind the scenes. Load flow data, voltage levels, power flow direction and fault level data are now available in ADMS on tap to operators for every component in the ADMS network diagram model, the results are per phase, covering current voltage, kW, kVA and kVAr.

The new issue is what to do with the masses of data now available, how to filter to the important data, and how and when to present the data to operators.

Time Warp Errors in Incremental Updates to the ADMS Network Model

The process of updating a diagram that is in active use for monitoring the real time network condition and the safety conditions surrounding workers currently working on that network, is itself a risky process. It is essential that no existing switch position or safety documents are 'lost' during the alterations to the connectivity within the database nor in the graphics on screen. The alteration, therefore, needs to be clinically defined in scope and the before and after conditions put through a checking and approval process before their implementation, and the change itself must be made in as near a momentary fashion as is possible to prevent random new changes coinciding with the planned change event. These criteria, therefore, exclude some of the normal IT methods of updating diagrams. It is for instance impractical to extract a complete layer of the diagram, alter it and slip it back in, this is a technique used in some GIS updates, but the time it takes and the need to recheck the complete network model excludes it as a real time technique. A real need to allow operations to check and approve the alteration also means that an automatic update from a master system is not viable. (This is a real need because operations staff could be held liable in a legal accident enquiry should a diagram change be an integral part of the reasons for an operational accident occurring.) Finally the distribution network is such a busy network, incremental changes occur nearly every day with thousands of changes being processed per year. This justified a complete management process within the operations system and this needs to be modelled within the ADMS. This criteria was a fundamental 'must have' requirement when the traditional wall diagram and handwritten paper processes and logging, (pre-1990), were being considered for conversion into an IT process. It became important again some twenty years later when standalone DMS was being redesigned into an ADMS concept, these real time sensitivities still required to be supported.

ADMS achieves this by the master GIS sending changes to the diagram to the DMS in advance of real time, thereby giving time for the operations staff to include the proposed change in a checking and approvals process. The remainder of the process, checking and approval and then the implementation of the change in real time, is essentially the same process as was first invented for DMS solution twenty years before.

The ADMS interface involves a CIM/GML technology to transfer network model changes into the DMS from GIS. This ensures synchronisation of assets between the master GIS and the DMS models. Within DMS, the process includes support for adding operational requirements to the graphic model, such as logic to model safety interlocks and the extra provisions for devices that will be monitored and remotely controlled by SCADA.

(There could be an automatic process added to the interface to enable DMS to automatically inform GIS when the connectivity has been permanently changed, triggering an automatic response from GIS updates, with the potential to reduce the massive manual update workload of GIS.)

This incremental update process involves preparation time in advance of real time, but it enables the actual real time changes to be done in under ten seconds which is suitable for real time operation. Possibly not all ADMS can achieve this update time, but certainly some can.

Over the years, real time systems have accommodated traditional procedures that caused even days of delay to relatively important updates and months of delays in trivial updates, such as registering the connectivity of one new customer. By focussing on the 'real time truth', developments have chipped away at the causes of time warp errors, lax business processes that caused time warp errors up to several hours have been under scrutiny and now there is technology and tight business processes available that can reduce time warp error down to seconds for most important transactions.

6.2 Connectivity Errors

Connectivity errors are an onsite connection that is different from what the ADMS network model shows. This implies a process failure in reporting the change or updating the change. (Note this is not just a time warp error delay in reporting, it is a total omission to capture the change, a flaw in the process.)

DMS Connectivity Errors

In Africa, a DMS network model was developed from photographs of the main control room schematic wall diagram. This was after all, the reference currently being used by the control engineers and should, therefore, have been, a reliable starting point. This network was manually built into the new DMS using its own graphic editing tools, and as part of the commissioning checks several circuits were fully surveyed on site. This survey discovered transformers connected to the line that were not present on the control room model. This is an example of a flawed process of capturing and recording incremental changes to the network. The benefit of introducing a DMS then, now an ADMS, is that incremental changes become embedded into the methods of working, the process of getting the transformer connected obliges the operatives to use the process as modelled in ADMS and, therefore, captures all incremental changes, except those of criminal or deliberate intent to undermine the process, usually to steal electricity. Finding errors is not a reason to stop, or even delay, the ADMS installation, because the ADMS will introduce a rigorous process for updating from that point forward, including correcting any errors found during commissioning.

GIS Connectivity Errors

With GIS recognised as the master database for network assets, most ADMS would commence building an operational model for the DMS functions from a GIS source. However, connectivity errors can also be caused by becoming embedded at the time of GIS data input from paper records, or GIS not properly capturing an 'as built' correction to the original proposed connectivity.

Wherever cables are congested either on busy urban street corners or close to substations, GIS has difficulty in ascertaining if cables cross each other or join in some way. GIS has no quick and easy check for connectivity issues during the process of data capture from paper records and connectivity errors can become embedded in DMS as a result of importing these undiscovered errors from GIS. Discovery

86

will occur when there are unexpected outcomes from network switching events, or may come to light by comparison with the old operations paper diagrams during the DMS pre-commissioning checks. Every installation of DMS from a GIS source, even when there are assurances of the quality of data in GIS, has been found to include connectivity errors when loaded into DMS, there are no known exceptions. DMS on the other hand has an immediate test of new connectivity because as soon as a switch is operated the expected result either occurs as modelled, or it does not, and the model is immediately proved right or wrong. Fortunately this usually occurs during DMS testing prior to go live.

Instances of GIS not receiving or not updating 'as built' corrections imply a fault in the process of obtaining and/or recording of changes into the GIS. This is a similar case to the DMS connectivity error case, either a flawed process allowing accidental non-reporting of as built corrections, or deliberate deception, connections made for the purposes of theft.

There is, therefore, a strong argument for even a master GIS to defer to DMS on connectivity issues, and a process of GIS requesting confirmations from DMS for congested area connectivity would help resolve GIS difficulties in these areas and reduce embedded connectivity errors.

Customer Connectivity Error

Customer connectivity was discussed previously as a time warp error, but it may also be totally missed, a flaw in capturing the connection at all. The problem is relatively easily addressed however. A periodic comparison can be run between the customer metering database and the OMS customer database to identify metered customer premises with no connectivity to a network supply point.

Granularity of Customer Connection – Per Phase Connectivity Errors

A second customer connectivity issue is the granularity of the data. The granularity of customer connection has been improving since the first OMS were installed in the 1990s. Then, a list of customer per secondary transformer was sufficient to ensure the crews were sent to the correct location. In later years expectations and technology improved and OMS requirement was refined to identify the LV feeder, the section of LV feeder, and now the phase connections become significant because of:

- Embedded micro-renewable energy generation
- The imminent availability of smart meter data
- The imminent increase in EV charging points

All of these three issues demand more accurate customer connectivity data. However, there are millions of customer connections and the truism is still relevant, it is just not worth the cost and effort to fund a huge deliberate data collection project to acquire this granularity. Fortunately there is another way, the data can be 'learned' and inferred during normal operations, and there is, therefore, a way to gradually improve connectivity data towards the per LV cable section per phase ideal. Post fault analysis will show that say 'red' phase LV fuse was found blown on an LV feeder. That implies that every caller who reported that fault has a connection on the red phase. The district clerk could, therefore, be given an additional task of reviewing LV faults to improve per phase connectivity. Also there are technological aides, devices that crews on site can apply at the service connection point which will determine the phase connection while they are present at a customer premises. The crews could be recording phase connection on to their Mobile system to automatically upload that data into the ADMS. By using both the post event research and the opportunities to collect data while on site, the improved granularity can become a gradually improving data set. These incremental strategies are more attractive than a deliberate data collection exercise because they are based on the opportunity cost of having a person at that location for a different purpose. The overall aim with customer connectivity is to prevent it eroding in accuracy over time, and to improve the data granularity down to per phase and per LV section. Reports will create the visibility and quantify the issue and rigorous management processes will keep their systems maintained to operate at optimal performance. An annual health check of data prior to the storm season, is a precaution used by many utilities to assess readiness for storms which are, in effect, an annual system stress test.

6.3 Potential Connectivity Errors in ADMS Update Processes

Overwriting Accurate Connectivity

A modern-day twist since the advent of ADMS, has been found where automatic updates of customer connectivity from GIS to DMS has overwritten connectivity proven to be correct within DMS. The DMS had proven the connectivity by discovery during fault events etc. and yet the GIS import overwrites this with embedded GIS errors. This re-introduces errors, it is too simplistic an implementation of an automated update procedure. Automated updates occur around the data categorised as trivial, such as individual customer connectivity updates. Trivial data updates bypass the DMS checks and approvals process and are inserted directly into the DMS database. There needs to be an additional defence to prevent the overwriting of customer connectivity known and proven to be accurate. This can be a concept used in some DMS of holding a 'fuzzy' connectivity data flag indicating that it is unproven, and proven connectivity where the data status flag is not shown. Automatic updates can proceed against 'fuzzy' data but attempts to update proven data should be resisted and referred back to GIS for update to the proven correct connectivity.

Relative Numbers of Database Network Components and Their Rate of Increase

Another issue concerns the number of components in the GIS database. A simple connection between switch A and switch B is held in the DMS as a connector, a single entity or possibly a series of underground and overhead single entities. (DMS needs to differentiate overhead from underground because different operational practices are possible on overhead lines and these need to be capable of being modelled.) GIS is more of an asset database and is, therefore, interested in each drum length of cable installed, its manufacturer etc. Therefore, GIS can hold multiple network components which are represented in DMS as either one underground connector or an overhead connector.

This difference can be handled in several ways:

- DMS can hold a 'table attribute' giving the ability to hold attributes of different GIS components within the umbrella of a single DMS connector component.
- GIS can do the sums in advance and send composite connector attributes to DMS.

Why is there a difference? DMS needs to always keep a focus on performing its processes fast so that operators do not perceive delays as they carry out their work, it needs to be real time. These processes include an assessment of the present connectivity status of the component and ascertaining if it is attached to a live source somewhere, or is dead or isolated or earthed, or indeed running in abnormal parallel. This process kicks in for every change of connectivity reported to DMS. The assessment follows from one component to the next and the time to completion is directly proportional to the number of components to be assessed. Increase in the number of components slows down DMS performance, it is that simple. Of course data processing has massively increased in speed over the years and a second way out of this dilemma is to depend on further processor speed improvement. However, there is an underlying problem in the way GIS treats connectors. Whenever a repair is done on an underground cable, it requires some five metres of faulty cable to be cut out and a new, five-metre section of cable to be inserted plus two connecting joints to remake the connectivity. DMS still 'sees' the same single connector, therefore, its database does not increase in size. GIS now has the original cable cut into two separate assets plus a new five-metre long cable asset and two joint assets, one database component has been replaced by five. Every year there are 4,000 cable faults representing a growth of 20,000 new components in GIS, extra to the growth seen by DMS.

6.4 Summary of Data Maintenance in ADMS

Therefore, using rigorous procedures and data maintenance methodology:

- SCADA updates are shown in seconds.
- Manual switching can be recorded in seconds (via mobile).
- Network diagram can be patched within seconds of a real time connection.
- Customer new connections can be updated with 24 hours.

This means that the data extracted and used to create automatic real time reports is nearly always by default, accurate. There will still be errors caused, for instance, by mistyping dates and times, but a simple process of monitoring for outlying data can be used to capture and correct these in an auditable way prior to publishing the reports.

These automated real time reports tend to cause a few initial embarrassments, but at least the managers are now managing the correct issues, and the metrics that emanate from the real time reports are really useful in driving up network performance figures. It is rarely the fault of crews when performance is low, it is usually delays in providing instruction or sending crews to the wrong initial location or to the wrong priority job, or logistics issues around the provision of the correct repair materials and tools. Provided the crews cooperate with timeous reporting of their actions the reports will identify areas where improvements are needed and, therefore, be an important driver towards better performance.

6.5 Maintenance of the Generic IT Aspects of ADMS

Some utilities try to bundle real time systems such as ADMS within the generic IT department duties, but others identify separate teams with both a knowledge of where the priorities lie in the power network, understand the impact of computer system degradation on power network performance and appreciate the differences from generic corporate IT systems:

- 24 x 7 availability
- The focus on real time performance
- Operational data security

These requirements can influence the utility to buy 'noncorporate standard' makes and types of computer server client workstations and operating systems and to have specialised support contracts with vendors.

Even though the ADMS may involve non-standard IT specification, these systems still need generic IT system maintenance of the main components:

- Server and client hardware – typical lifespan five to 15 years.
- Operating systems software – typical supported versions three years.
- Application software – very variable in its maintenance requirements.
- Third-party software, e.g. the relational database software version.
- Security software – typically supported versions change as the threats change.

On obvious, conclusion can be drawn that the more IT systems that exist in the utility, there will be more complexity and workload in maintaining each of these five generic areas per system. There is, therefore, a massive advantage in simplifying IT maintenance and reducing IT maintenance costs, if a large system such as DMS can be handled as ONE product rather than a combination of three to five or seven products that interface together. This is an area of genuine differentiation between ADMS vendors, some deliver ADMS by interfacing separate products e.g. SCADA, OMS, Switching Management, Network Analysis and they may reduce the data upkeep by using standard plug-in interface technology via middleware systems, but the main IT maintenance issues remain a per product set of costs. Other ADMS are developed as one product, one version of application software which when upgraded to a new version upgrades all the SCADA, switching management, OMS and network analysis functions are de facto included in the one upgrade. The one third party relational database performs its purpose for all functions. It is true that an 'integrated' ADMS will include some specialised servers to prevent performance contamination to other processes, but in general an integrated ADMS will use less IT hardware than an interfaced multiple product ADMS. Also from a security perspective there is one consistent surface to be protected from intrusion, rather than the individual surfaces of multiple products.

7

Non Functional Requirements of DMS

7.1. Flexible Architecture and Deployment

Although centralisation was a big part of the business case for DMS, the ability to have different types of operator all gain access to the system for their own purposes and from their own working location introduced requirements for flexible working. These would enable the company to anticipate a storm and increase the manning levels not just of linemen and contractors but also for control engineers and dispatchers. Some electricity distribution companies expanded by acquisition or merger with others and the one corporate entity may control different MV networks hundreds of miles apart. One such company put in place a DMS for each location but an IT infrastructure that enabled operators on one system to flip their workstation over and access the remote DMS as an extra controller or dispatcher.

Due to their geographical separation a storm hitting one region rarely hit the other and, therefore, they had a built-in expansion capability to provide remote help with control and OMS dispatch.

There is also the need to allow for disaster recovery. How does a control room still manage to be effective when it, itself has been hit by an earthquake? A disaster recovery site is an alternative venue with a complete running version showing the same network state as the operational one. It merely needs operators to connect their workstations to it and the control functions can continue. One way to allow for disaster recovery is to have a DMS server or servers in a remote location rarely hit by the same weather features at the same time, another is to distribute operators and servers so that there is a better chance of some of them escaping the disaster.

A DMS architecture should be flexible enough not to constrain the thinking within the company on how to provide disaster recovery. In this way different companies can find resilience solutions to fit their specific sets of risks. A common mistake when considering these options is the misconception of dual redundancy. Dual redundancy assumes that if one element fails then the other automatically takes the strain and continues. By positioning main servers in different sites there is dual redundancy of sites but the communications between the servers needs to be dual redundant too and there have been occasions where both communication channels, were actually two separate cores within the one cable. A strike on the cable removes both channels, therefore, this was not a viable dual redundant solution.

7.2 Reliability and Resilience

Other than the architecture, the functional requirements of DMS also need to be reliable and resilient to either software or component failure. The DMS requires to match the reliability of a permanent control room building with its permanent wall diagrams, it needs to be 24 x 7 x 365 continuously available. How was a computer system in the early 1990s going to match this level of reliability when everyone knew that SCADA systems still incurred about a week of downtime per year? A distribution management system needed to be 24 x 7 with an annual downtime in minutes rather than hours or days. This has been achieved using multiple servers across multiple locations and a variety of methods of keeping these server synchronised, or batch updated. Electricity distribution companies selecting a DMS need to investigate the methods used by their potential IT vendors on how reliability and resilience are delivered and examine the figures on the reliability achieved. Today, resilience to a single failure should be non-disruptive to the business and reliability should be capable of achieving under 20 minutes unplanned system downtime per year, an availability of 99.997%.

A traditional method of calculating reliability was to examine the mean time between failures data provided by hardware manufacturers. This would be fine in a single site environment, however, with the combination of multiple sites, the communications networks, multiple servers provided near seamless resilience when a failure does occur, MTBF is today all but meaningless. The practical requirement is that the operators can continue to do their work at their normal speed. Operator workstations can sense the loss of their connection to a server and can automatically search the network and connect themselves to another DMS server within a few seconds and enable the operator to continue controlling from where they left off on the other server. This resilience has been extended to SCADA with dual front end processors, the ability to have an alternative communication channels to alternative FEPs and installing RTUs which support dual port operation.

7.3 Back Up Tapes of DMS Transactions

There are so many transactions occurring per day that the ability to take back up versions of the DMS is essential. The ability to back up in early DMS, varied from a requirement to take the system down, a requirement to flip the system on to its alternate servers involving some down time. The utilities prefer a method that does not disturb ongoing operations and systems offering that are available; some of these systems have software which can seamlessly remove a server for back up purposes, from the operational server group, the remaining servers automatically compensate for its absence.

7.4 Real Time Performance

The DMS only began to succeed as a concept when it could match and better the speed at which control operators need to work. The performance of the network diagram in displaying changes of state was a crucial area where real time compliance was difficult to achieve but essential. Control engineers could scan a schematic wall diagram by eye in seconds and understand the scope of an outage. The original computer attempts at doing this were abysmal failures particularly when the outages were large (ironically, that is when the DMS is needed most). Connectivity tracing, was the mechanism for establishing the extent of an outage and each component assessment was an individually processed transaction. Therefore, tracing was directly proportional to the number of components needing to be checked and speed of the server processor. Smarter analysis and improved processing speeds were the key to complying with the requirements for real time performance. These requirements could not be met by some EMS, because their diagrams were originally developed for smaller network models, nor by some DMS and OMS based on GIS network models, which were developed to cope with masses of data without a real time requirement. In the early days, performance was improved by reducing the number of components within the DMS network model to only those of operational significance, modelled as a schematic. The improvements in processor speeds over the years have been massive and this has enabled more systems to achieve an acceptable operating speed using GIS networks for their DMS, however, the GIS based performance is bound to degrade over time due to the growth in components as faults are repaired.

7.5 Productised Software

Another non-functional requirement that not even the utility industry recognised, but the IT industry introduced, was the 'productisation' of the software.

Early software development techniques, rather like the early hand built cars, were designed and customised for each customer, particularly with SCADA and the transmission system EMS applications. Each utility customer needed something subtly different from other utilities so the code was heavily customised for each installation. DMS software was a next stage of software development, and it provided a 'production line' process just like the transition from bespoke car building to the Ford production line in cars, and this provided the opportunity to attempt to write code as a repeatable product with no bespoke or customised additions specific to one customer's installed version. When new features or changes were identified, they would be added as a development of the core product back in the software development environment, and then made available to all customers as an upgraded software version. The software was also made flexible to use by being written in a specific way that enabled different options to be achieved from the same code by employing configuration of multiple tables of data.

Most vendors offer productised code, however, utility customers need to check and test the extent and validity of the productisation achieved by IT vendors. Many older systems were first installed as bespoke systems and they had a 'fit and forget' approach. Changes were only possible on as per installed system basis and were expensive and slow to implement. As the need for more changes grew over the years the installation would eventually be replaced by a new procurement and implementation project approximately every seven years. With productised code, changes are made available to customers via a relatively simple and short upgrade process, avoiding the need to restart a procurement process and avoiding yet another IT implementation project.

One way of testing the productisation of the code is to ask existing customers when they last upgraded, how often they upgrade and how long it takes. For some companies, upgrades are medium-sized projects lasting six months to a year, for others with more rigorous productisation, they are maintenance activities lasting a few days or weeks. The longer the delay between upgrades the larger the upgrade task. Companies tend to be offered upgrades annually but many only take them up when the new content is relevant to their business, and this can be two or three years between upgrades. Upgrades have been done after five years and while this can still be achieved as a maintenance task, there is a lot more prechecking and planning to be done than for a one-year upgrade.

Systems that started life as bespoke applications, allowing individual customisations of the code per customer installation, have let the genie out of the bottle and it is very tricky to put him back in! A quality management system regulating how code is written and extended is an essential component of delivering consistent productised code and the QMS needs to apply from the start of new software development.

Truly productised code is a major advantage, but is still hardly recognised in the industry today. Utility IT departments put great store in obtaining a very complete specification for their applications and looking as far into the future as they could reasonably project to include possible new functions in their specification. This was because nearly all of the vendors followed a 'fit and forget' approach to releasing their products. They would be installed, support contracts would fix bugs etc. but new changes might be able to be patched in as a customised project but this was difficult and time consuming and expensive. It also meant that, at procurement, complete compliance with this specification was very important. To win, the vendors had to be flexible in their language of compliance and hope to finesse the issues through customised demonstrations which could be mocked up in a few weeks but would take months to years to embed formally in their products.

Vendors with truly productised code could be more relaxed and define what was in the current released version, what was coming in the next release programme etc. and incrementally develop their product toward the specification required. Although this was actually a step change improvement in how software was delivered at that time, it was ahead of its time and many utility IT departments were too distrustful of the approach to adopt it, and these solutions lost out in the compliance scoring.

The effect of this nervousness, was to drive up the price of the procurement, both in developing and buying a large specification, and in the final cost of the winning solution. In fact many of the features would not be needed or lie unused for years, reducing the cost benefit of the procurement. The integrated productised approach could deliver current version providing over 80% compliance off the shelf, and provide a programme of upgrades delivering enhancements up to 100%

compliance, through the productised upgrade maintenance contracts. This flexibility removed the importance of trying to fit all the future requirements into the current version, once the utility realised that functions were incrementally added as and when needed, and introduced as a simple version upgrade through the maintenance contract. But this remains a difficult sell to this day and it requires a lot of interaction building up the potential customer's knowledge of the product, trust in the company and verification from existing customers. However, there are DMS customers today whose system was first purchased in the 1990s, who have not needed to go out to procurement to replace it or update it because every year or so they opt to take the software upgrade and move their system forward. Hardware upgrades and operating system upgrades are accommodated during the software upgrade as appropriate.

All vendors will describe their software as productised but the test of it is in the work involved in performing the upgrade and obtaining an operational system on completion. Many such companies are actually undertaking a mini for full re-implementation project, whereas a truly integrated and productised code can be upgraded in hours, following of course the pre testing and pre planning which can take three to four weeks or longer dependent on the complexity of the installation and the time since the previous upgrade.

The real advantage of this ease of upgrade became more noticeable as the Smart Grid concept was introduced and nearly simultaneously, the companies were being required to reduce their carbon footprint. This implied a journey of innovation introducing some 20 or so new applications and features which DMS would either have to add or interface to, within the target period to 2020. A product strategy which involves a seven year 'fit and forget' and then re-install with a new product version cannot cope with the quantity or rate of change needed in DMS by 2020. The incremental development platform offered by productised software is ideally suited to delivering these new functions into the product and making them available to existing customers via simple version upgrades.

7.6 Integrated Systems

Originally SCADA was standalone, OMS was standalone, and switching management was paper based. Operators were jumping between systems, with different user interfaces, multiple keyboards with different uses for the functional keys etc. Add to this the telephone and radio systems and paper based processes all adding complexity to the operator's role. The IT workload was also becoming very complex with multiple diagrams and databases and differently written code per application with different updating and upgrading cycles and maintenance routines. The business case was made based on operator ease of use and ease of IT maintenance to seek more integrated solutions for DMS.

There have been four approaches to integration:

- Desktop integration
- Point to point interfacing between applications
- Middleware with plug in standard interfaces between applications

- Factory based integration of the applications at the software level

Desktop integration was a wires-based approach enabling the operator to toggle between applications on a common user workstation, common set of screens, a common mouse and a common keyboard. This solution does nothing to reduce the complexity 'under the desk', nor does it reduce the difficulties in maintaining and synchronising multiple systems.

Interfaces enabling one application to access the other sharing a user workstation and possibly standardising a user interface. This solution begins to address the duplications of diagram maintenance, data maintenance between systems but the more applications involved the more complex the interfacing becomes.

Interface complexity was addressed by introducing a middleware information bus. Each application could publish its data to the bus and subscribe to data from other applications directly from the bus. Each application, therefore, only needed the one standard interface defining what is was publishing and to what it was subscribing. This solution introduces a middleware bus which is expensive and adds infrastructure to the IT solution. However, the basic properties of interfaces are not avoided, they can report inconsistencies between systems, but they cannot cure them. For instance a SCADA diagram has a newly commissioned switch, in place of an old manual switch, and there is an interface on to the middleware which now publishes data related to that switch. The OMS is written in different code, possibly even in a different country, and using a different network diagram. Has the OMS diagram been updated to show the new switch? Did this happen at the same time as the SCADA diagram altered? If there is a difference, a time when OMS is still using the old manual switch, when SCADA is using its new automated switch then the interface will report the difference and leave it to the operator to fix or workaround. This applies to diagrams and databases, and then there is the upgrade to new versions, and coping with new subfunctions introduced through the upgrades. From an IT vendor software perspective it is fine, the code is all tested and it works, however, the customer utility is left with the difficult to impossible task of synchronising data and diagram updates between systems and coping with the outages for upgrading of each part of their DMS. Middleware is a solution which cures a symptom but not the root cause of complexity.

The Factory Based Integration Solution

This solution recognised early on, the limitations of external interfaces and these vendors sought to minimise the use of these interfaces to the minimum. This analysis drew them to the conclusion that all real time applications were better integrated at the product level leaving external interfaces to interact with non-real time applications. They developed a suite of DMS functions all in the same codebase with the interaction between them, the interfaces, already accounted for within the code, so that all functions could directly interact with the other DMS functions and share a common network diagram model and relational database. The external interfaces were, therefore, reduced in number and devoted to interaction with external non real time applications such as GIS and AMS etc. This solution is more expensive to produce for the vendor, but its major advantages are that it delivers much needed simplification to its utility customers. The DMS applications are always synchronised, one point of data update to the diagram and or database and all applications use that change immediately. One software upgrade upgrades all DMS functions simultaneously to the new version.

These integrated solutions have become the benchmark, the other solutions are adding to their offerings to synchronise data and diagram changes and seeking to integrate their code within the DMS functions.

From 2001 onwards, it was apparent that the decision to productise the code and the decision to integrate the functional applications were delivering more benefits of great value to utilities. Utilities were being measured on their network reliability, CAIDI CAIFI etc. and regulators began to publish the performance of utilities within their areas. This provided an opportunity for the companies and the IT vendors to check whether their DMS investments were delivering end product benefits as seen by customers in terms of reduced customer minutes lost and customer interruptions. Within a few years of independently published results it was becoming clear that the integrated solution of having switching management, outage management and SCADA all integrated within one DMS product was outperforming installations where these three functions were separate products interfaced together.

7.7 Tolerance of Poor or Missing Data

Rubbish in rubbish out is a well-known mantra of the IT environment. This is important and true for functions like

SCADA and NMS switching management where there is a binary difference, a switch is open or closed. SCADA cannot function if an operator intends to open switch A but that action actually opens switch B. This would be intolerable. However, within OMS, and DPF there are useful methods, and good reasons, to use elements of intelligent guesswork to ensure a result is obtained. OMS may be holding say, 1.5 million customer addresses, it is reasonable to expect the OMS call clustering algorithms to still work even if a few of these addresses have no, or incorrect, connectivity. OMS uses the concept of flagging estimated connectivity as 'fuzzy', and the algorithm programme includes instructions on how to treat fuzzy data. Note that fuzzy connectivity can be used at customer connection level because each single customer is insignificant in comparison to the whole number of customers off supply and the whole customer database, but fuzziness cannot be applied to MV connectivity because this would impact thousands of customers and throw the clustering algorithm on to the wrong assumption. Similarly when running a load flow calculation, with thousands of MV circuits and hundreds of thousands possibly millions of individual network components, the calculation would fail to converge if a single cable is missing its cross sectional area or its length attributes. Academically, this might be a desirable outcome, but for a real time load flow on a live control room diagram, obtaining an answer is far more important, and the probable error incurred may well be insignificant. In this case the concept of 'default values' fills in the missing data and uses intelligent guesses based on the averages or most common data in use around them. Data tolerance in these two functions is essential for their operation in a real practical situation. If these functions are data brittle, they will break down and be of much less use to the utility. When these functions are data tolerant and are written in a way which is pragmatic about some level of missing data, the utility obtains better use of their investment. Data tolerance does place extra work on users of these functions, however, this is preferable to the users being faced with a total non-function of their programme.

8

Extracting Added Value from ADMS

8.1 ADMS Data

In the process of managing the network, a lot of data ends up stored in the ADMS. Some companies use it better than others. The ADMS is not some trophy to put on a shelf or in a display cabinet so that visitors might be impressed with how forward looking the company is. The ADMS is a reservoir of data and real time information, a tool to be used. The best companies encourage their staff to feed the system with real time data and encourage anyone looking for information, not to interrupt a crew or a control engineer with questions, but to access the ADMS data via reports or real time dashboards and summaries to find the data they need.

ADMS data is the lifeblood pulsing around the company, and the company becomes energised as this data is used, just like an athlete gasping in air and oxygenating their blood and rejuvenating their muscles.

I have heard asset managers bemoaning how difficult it is to get crews to report asset damage. That is because they want crews to fill in a defect form and send it to them, when in fact the crew could have already reported the defect into ADMS as part of an incident investigation or a fault report. The crews should not be asked to have multiple masters and multiple systems to update, they need a simple interface directly into the corporate systems from their mobile and leave the different departments to their own devices to obtain that data out of the ADMS.

I have heard of departments of incident researchers correcting and updating data from OMS after a storm has ended. This was happening so that a final situation report could be produced to convince the regulatory bodies that a state of emergency had occurred and special dispensations should be granted after the event. If the data had been correctly input and consistently collected in real time, there wouldn't be a need for duplicate data entry investigations, for finding missing data and for error corrections. This whole process, the creation of this department with a dozen researchers, would not be needed is the original process was re-examined and time warp errors eliminated from it by the use of modern technology. This wasteful process and waste of staff just covered up missing functionality from the OMS and missing technology that could make it efficient for the crews to update simply into a hand held mobile device once, and then forget it and carry on restoring customers. This case study was a most effective business case for replacing a first-generation standalone OMS with a modern OMS as an integrated function within ADMS.

8.2 Data Configuration

Providing the ability to configure data in different ways is an efficient method of writing software code. Rather than having a new line of code for every colour of line on the diagram, the code merely points to a colour table which can be configured and new rows to the table can be added by staff trained in configuration. This is a facile example but the principle is very powerful, one section of code can, therefore, be interpreted through a series of data configuration tables in countless different ways. The new code written into a new version of the product can define the changes to the tables, adding new columns and specifying how the new features interact with the existing code and other tables, then data maintenance staff trained in data configuration can set up the new features all within the newly upgraded code version, by populating the new entries into tables.

This is potentially very powerful for the customer utility. Once they have their own staff training in configuration, then many changes to the ADMS can be effected without invoking new software development costs, risks and delays. The first question asked by analysts when faced with a request for something new is 'is it configurable?'

Configuration is fast and involves less risk, there is no new code to test and debug. There is a risk when the proposed new configuration is so complicated and clunky that it can impact on system performance and in these cases new development is the better option.

Configuration is a very powerful concept and it is essential for a utility to train staff to be expert in data configuration, if they are to maximise the potential of their ADMS investment.

8.3 Interface and/or Reports into Asset Management

The ADMS holds loading data on every network component of the live operational network. Some of that data is remotely measured by SCADA, and some is calculated by on line network analysis, distribution power flow calculations (DPF).

ADMS also holds events such as alarms indicating near limit and over limit loading of these assets, with the ability to ascertain if the network was running in normal or abnormal configuration at the time.

This data is collected in near real time and stored as half hour averages over several years.

The Asset Management team can obtain access to this data over an interface or via reports and produce loading trends per feeder/primary substation/bulk supply point and forecast future capacity problems at pinch points in the network. This enables the design work and site acquisition work in obtaining new locations for BSPs and Primary substations to be started timeously and avoid expensive time pressured property purchases that could be incurred if nothing happened until the overloads occurred.

Designers could also use the data to make sense of embedded generation and its impact on loading, or nett generation from some sources.

Using the switching data from NMS, asset managers can obtain reports of actual numbers of operations of all switchable devices on the network and whether that operation was a normal load operation or operated under fault conditions. Asset managers could have their criteria for maintenance per device actually stored as attributes within the ADMS network diagram and as the maintenance threshold is approached the ADMS could pass out a request for a device to be included in the maintenance program.

Both the loading and the frequency of usage data can also be used to identify underused and under loaded networks.

OMS holds data on every fault, complete with a fault report that can include root cause of the fault, and the reliability impact per fault on Customer Interruptions and Customer Minutes Lost. Again asset managers can obtain this data over interfaces or reports and make strategic decisions on maintain/ replace/ redesign networks to obtain improvements in reliability over time.

8.4 Interface with Smart Meter Management Systems (MMS)

The MMS in UK is an IT system developed as a generic function to be used by all companies. The DNOs will have to pay to access the data from the MMS. It is, therefore, important that the numbers of applications and frequency with which these applications need metering data be minimised to keep down cost for the DNO and impact on the MMS for the metering authority.

Metering data on its own is useful for billing for energy usage, but the DNOs have uses for the data to ascertain usage per LV cable and per secondary substation. To achieve this there needs to be a combination of metering data and connectivity data. Since the connectivity can be dynamic, it is important that the summations of meter data reflect the connectivity at the time of consumption, and also the ability to hold connectivity data per phase becomes important when attempting to synthesise the loading of an LV feeder and secondary substation from meter readings. It is true that the connectivity of individual premises to the nearest LV cable rarely if ever changes, but there are approximately 16,000 LV faults per year in a DNO and these can involve abnormal feeding arrangements being put in place to assist in locating and isolating the fault, so there will be this continuous error occurring at random locations where faults occur. There is also unmetered supplies such as landlords' supplies and street lighting, technical losses, and unquantified local renewable generation which can upset the results of simple addition of metering data. These are the potential errors within the first 250m from premise up through the LV network to the secondary substation. Above the secondary substation the MV connectivity allows the secondary substation loads to be added to synthesize an MV feeder load and this can now be compared with the SCADA measurement at the source of the MV feeder. The ADMS is, therefore, the optimal IT system to interface with MMS, because ADMS holds the accurate real time connectivity of the networks and the accurate fault status in real time. ADMS also has the LV network diagram which can be updated and annotated by crews using the Mobile application, providing a collaborative control over the

LV network without the need to involve the operations control room which traditionally controls MV and HV networks. The ADMS has a load profile for every secondary substation which is currently estimated from available data and statistics. The accuracy of these profiles is variable and needs regular monitoring. However, if the data from MMS was introduced via a background process over an interface, the data could be summated and stored as the 'correct' load profile per substation, improving the confidence and accuracy of the data and the DPF results. Every other IT application that needs metering data for reasons other than metering can obtain access to the ADMS secondary substation load profiles for the data. This also ensures the anonymity of individual customer's data and enables compliance with data protection legislation.

8.5 The Improved Management of the LV Network

As has been mentioned the LV network is largely ignored by the operations control room other than when it can be used to back feed customers off supply or when ensuring sections of network are fully isolated, in relation to MV operations which are within the remit of the control room. The LV network is very loosely managed locally in depots by a discipline of returning temporary open points back to normal open points after work has been completed. There is little monitoring that all of this is rigorously undertaken on every occasion and the network has been known to degrade significantly from its normal configuration over time.

However, the LV network is largely worked on while it is live, and as such it is of continuous interest to the Health and Safety Executive who are nervous of the potentially dangerous working conditions for staff and for the public. The DNOs cannot afford to have an HSE order banning live work at LV, because the disruptions to supplies would be huge, but neither can the DNO afford the same control environment in place for MV to operate over the LV network it is too large, and it has four times the volume of work done on it compared to the MV network. The final component of the perfect storm is the added complexities of local renewable generation, mainly domestic solar, but also small scale wind generation and micro hydro schemes.

Generation at LV is a major factor in reducing network losses because suddenly some or all of the energy consumed in a premises is not passing through the distribution networks and, therefore, not causing network losses. The problems arise within the LV network. The loading and importantly the per phase balance of the LV network is set during design, designers allow service connections per phase and stick to a rota of connections that ensures per phase balance over every six connections, following the convention RYBBYR red phase, yellow then blue and the reversing the next three connections BYR so that over six house connections, all things being averaged, there should be negligible current on the neutral connection in the main cable. This is fine in theory, the cable jointers, in practice, do not always follow the specified phase balancing because the phase specified may be in an awkward position at the point where the cable is opened up for the joint to be made. Jointers, therefore, have been known to differ from their instruction but they themselves then vary the phasing at the adjacent joints when they come to connect them. However, the consistency along the whole feeder cannot be guaranteed because it can easily be different jointers sent out to make connections over the weeks that the houses are built and completed. The introduction of solar panels, however, has undermined even the designer's theoretical phase balancing. Customers will randomly decide to connect solar panels, usually if their roof is pitched to enable south facing slopes for the panels. Gradually, throughout a housing estate, some of the houses with an appropriate roof pitch will take on solar generation and that house, instead of consuming, say 2KW on red phase, is generating on to red phase. Best case the house load just looks to be low, worst case the house becomes a negative load and this reversal upsets the balance on the neutral core of the main cable, and the summation of phase load currents on the main cable. Around a housing estate of 100 houses the phase balance is, therefore, upset randomly dependent on which houses have a south facing roof and how many of these customer install solar panels.

Phase imbalance will produce per phase voltage differences between phases at remote ends such as network boxes and pillars. There is now an unmeasured quality problem on the LV network that might led to overloading the neutral core, high or low voltages at remote ends.

These three pressures, safety, cost and phase imbalance due to solar generation, are driving new interest in improving control and monitoring of the LV network, and the challenge has been to find a cost effective method of delivering this.

The ADMS does support the ability to hold an LV network diagram in addition to the MV and HV networks and can operate them so that interconnectedness is modelled between them. (an MV fault will make the LV network diagram lose its power inputs from the secondary substations affected by the MV fault, an LV parallel between two secondary substations can show as a temporary looped supply condition on the MV network, assuming the LV switching to make the parallel is recorded as a switching action in the ADMS) The ADMS supports a per phase representation of the LV network which will correctly identify partially live cables when for instance a report is received that a fuse is blown. The game changer, the concept that enables LV control without impacting on the workload of control engineers, is mobile. The crews can used mobile to access the NMS switching functions and create their own switching schedules for the LV network or use it as a log of switching they undertake in pursuit of a fault. Now there is an instant visibility of the actions of every crew working on the LV network because the crews record their actions into their mobile device, which automatically sends these updates back to the ADMS LV network diagram updating its connectivity and logging the switching times and operator ID. Each job can have a flag configured indicating abnormal connectivity has been applied and this flag will prevent the job from being closed down until normal connectivity has been restored or a new normal connectivity is configured. The collaborations between crews coordinated via the ADMS functions and network diagram provide the improved visibility and control over the LV networks without the need for a centralised control person, this is collaborative control between the crews and between crews and ADMS via mobile.

The added value of this concept is that all of ADMS functions then operate over the LV network as well; OMS LV faults can be visualised and tracked, DPF load flow calculations can be undertaken and solar generation can be modelled and included as generation points. The crews can also use on site devices to identify connected phase and mobile can upload that data so that phase connectivity can be improved.

8.6 The Achievement of Real Time Truth

The development of the functions of ADMS have all driven towards removing the confusion between what crews see and experience on site, and what the control engineers are led to believe from looking at a model of the network, and what senior management might understand from their perspective in the board room or major incident room.

In a storm, a SCADA system might have reported 100 trips, but the NMS might have 200 fault jobs in progress and OMS might have 500 incidents to investigate. An incident room manager would look at these three statistics and be confused, what is the true state of the network now? Coping strategies such as devolving control to teams on site, mean that the centre is starved of progress updates until the crews find time to call it in. By focussing on the operational data update processes, identifying time warp errors and eliminating them, the ADMS becomes a more reliable method of understanding the situation. ADMS can now produce dynamic dashboards of information and one real time report, the best, the most consistent, source of real time information to managers. This report is updated directly by crews with mobile handsets, complemented by SCADA, on line load flow calculations and dynamic calculations of customer minutes lost per restoration stage per incident. This ADMS information tool provides the incident room manager with a dashboard of key data, all of it consistent and as accurate as current technology can make it. Now the development of strategic responses to storms can be better managed, delays and costs can be eliminated and customers can be restored faster. There is no justifiable reason to lose control or visibility of the state of the network, nor the numbers of customers off supply, even in the midst of a hurricane. Supplies might be off, crews cannot be safely deployed, but the ADMS data will inform them accurately of current state and where to start.

9

ADMS Yesterday, Today and Tomorrow

This has been a story of software development supporting the emerging needs of the electricity distribution industry over some 30 years. This industry is relatively new, only starting within the twentieth century. In Western Europe, its major expansion, 'Electricity for All', occurred between the 1950s and early 1970s. The late 70s into the 1980s saw a focus change towards better productivity both in terms of labour management, and the introduction of new materials, and new mechanisation technology reducing the time it took to joint cables, dig tracks, build overhead lines and find faults.

Major investment in distribution was, however, limited by the more attractive returns available from investing in transmission and in generation. Distribution was, figuratively speaking, living off the scraps that fell from the corporate investment table. SCADA for distribution being a case in point, this was made possible because the major investment case for SCADA was made for generation and transmission, and this included the ability to quickly load shed Distribution Primary transformers, if an emergency instability at EHV occurred. Since the SCADA installation, therefore, reached the Distribution Primary substations, any spare capacity they then had in the installed system could be used to deploy SCADA into Distribution Primary MV feeder circuit breakers as well.

As big monopolies do, the electricity industry diversified into its own communications and its own IT development departments. By the end of the 1980s most electricity distribution organisations had their own IT departments employing hundreds of computing engineers.

The 1990s changed all this due to three major shocks to hit the distribution industry:

- Political change introduced privatisation which drove company restructuring and staff downsizing to save operating costs, forcing the industry to focus on its core activities and spin off their new communications and IT departments into unregulated businesses.
- Regulatory oversight of natural monopolies, such as electricity distribution, drove reporting accuracy and incentivised performance improvement.
- Climate change drove innovation to reduce the carbon footprint of the industry, replacing almost all investment in fossil fuelled power stations with renewable energy, some of it embedded within the distribution network.

The 1990s is also when the information age overtook the industrial age which had lasted 160 years.

It was the Information Age that delivered, and continues to deliver, the solutions to these three major shocks.

Privatisation reduced staff by 30% in under five years, centralised Customer call centres and Control rooms, reducing a three-tier management structure into two tiers, and stripped out whole departments of non-core activities such as IT, centralising customer service and network operations control and asset management. The second tier was largely involved in delivery of the electricity, new construction, maintenance and emergency response to faults. The staff remaining were those generally under 50 and there was a massive loss of local knowledge and engineering expertise. This was compensated for by embedding that knowledge into new IT systems that could model 'best practice processes'. IT systems then enabled the centralisation strategy without losing the benefits of local knowledge or the expertise. For asset management this meant an IT programme to introduce Asset Management systems and GIS. For Customer service this meant the introduction of a new CRM system to support the centralised Call centre. For network operations this meant the first functions of Distribution Management Systems to support the centralisation into one control room.

- Safety Logic and safety documents management.
- Switching management of planned outages.
- Unplanned outage and storm management.
- Network model management.
- Interfacing to SCADA (originally) and to the call centre.

This major investment in electricity distribution IT systems did make a business case comparable to the large generation and transmission investments, because each IT development was immediately impactful across the complete distribution network and organisation as soon as it was commissioned and massive savings and performance improvement was evident within a year. This was a series of step change improvements for the industry, rather than a gradual process of change, the return on investments was, large, visible, attractive and quick. More importantly they were major enablers in delivering the company restructuring strategy to a centralised core with a second tier focussing on delivery.

These IT projects each delivered staff and cost reductions, process improvement and the ability to control the reliability and standard of the process output. Customer service, asset management and asset operations were the three major investments and the combination of functions developed for asset operations became the DMS and eventually the ADMS as asset management began to seek closer access to operations data and enable more efficiencies by becoming master of the network model.

As an example of the scale of change experienced, the traditional outage management process would start with a local district call centre receiving a cluster of calls all within, say fifteen minutes. The call centre supervisor would be alerted and compile notes of these calls and send them bundled in a bulldog clip to the distribution executive engineer. Then an experienced engineer with local knowledge would attempt to locate the parts of the network affected using their knowledge of the local vicinity, the customers, and try to translate that on to the wall mounted schematic diagram of the network. Once there was an assessment of where to begin looking, a request would be made to the work supervisor to find a crew to investigate. They would check who was available locally and assess which tasks could be stopped to allow the crew to investigate this new fault and they would send that crew out. This process, to the point where a crew is dispatched, would take typically 15 to 30 minutes to achieve. The OMS IT system used the network model implemented originally to control the switching management process and added customer premise connections data to each secondary transformer on the diagram. Typically, this would be a list of known addresses supplied from that transformer. The customer calls meantime were now all captured on line in the new CRM system and an interface shared this data with OMS in seconds as each call was logged. OMS identified the addresses of the calls and matched them up to the transformers supplying them, and an algorithm began to look for patterns what would suggest the scope of the outage(s) by the algorithmic groupings. OMS would create an alert to engage an OMS operator and prompt them to create a new incident (consistent business process) and find a crew. OMS would automatically filter a list of available crews and the operator would select one and communicate directly with them. The OMS prompted the operator with all the necessary information the crew would need and the crew would accept the job and OMS would log the fact that the crew was assigned and dispatched. This process takes under five minutes. Even before the crew start investigating, a massive 10 to 25 minutes is saved from the duration of the outage by faster, automated processing of the incoming data. 4,000MV faults, 16,000LV faults and 60,000 single premise incidents a year, all benefited from this automated process every year saving around 1,600,000 customer minutes lost, and enabling staff reductions. The network statistics for customer minutes lost dropped by 30% in year one of OMS roll out despite loss of local presence in the new centralised operation and fewer staff employed.

Regulatory oversight, drove reporting and performance improvement. To be fair to the newly privatised Distribution Network Operators (DNOs), the investors seeking better returns on their investment also had a large influence on driving performance improvement because investors looked for the best network performance as an indicator of the better companies in which to invest. The IT industry working closely with the users of their systems in the control rooms jointly developed a much improved intelligent automation product that was capable of widespread deployment without a proportional increase in risk or in the cost of running the automation system.

The main issue with automated response to circuit breaker trips is that a possible cause of the trip might leave either the public or some workers in danger and, therefore, there is usually a delay while the control room assess whether it is safe to proceed. What intelligent automation did was to codify the safety checks that the best control engineers undertook, and make the DMS run these checks through its current data regarding who was working where, recent switching activity etc. With these types of questions asked of the current data, DMS then made the decision to abort or allow an automated response to proceed. This recognition of the safety issues enabled intelligent automation to win acceptance as a safe procedure and it became widely adopted and commissioned on to thousands of MV circuits over the several years.

The second issue in automation schemes is how to maintain them. Original automation schemes were based remotely in substations using a rigid ladder logic to follow a certain sequence of steps to isolate the fault and restore as many supplies as possible. This rigid automated sequence is dependent on the configuration of the circuit being in its normal standard state. Every time a new switch was added to the network, then a visit had to be made to the substation to reprogramme the automation with new logic, test it and recommission it. If there was a mass roll out of such schemes it is readily foreseen that the maintenance activity also rises proportionally, and rising operational costs when the overall Regulatory requirement was to reduce operating cost by 3% year on year meant that such a deployment would not gain approval. Also, when work was planned to have an outage on that feeder, then automation system had to be disabled prior to starting, and then someone had to remember to re-arm the automation system once the system was normal. Finally of course, the new central control room is left totally unaware of what the remote logic has ended up doing and the main DMS network model is now wrong. There is no OMS incident created to count customer minutes lost, there is no report created. Intelligent automation solved all of these issues. The logic itself is intelligent and flexible, it 'discovers' the scope of the tripped circuit and, as it does so, it discovers where the fault might be based on fault passage indicators situated around the network, and it discovers all the possible points from which an alternative supply might restore some of the supplies. This totally removes the rigidity of the logic and removes the necessity to only apply the automation when the circuit is running normally, discovery will identify the possible options irrespective of the current state of the surrounding network. There is no need, therefore, for maintenance trips to reprogramme logic, therefore, maintenance costs do not rise in proportion to the size of the roll out of automation. Since the logic is no longer based in the substations, but in the main DMS servers in the control room, then DMS is made aware of intelligent automation being triggered, it does record the switching actions and create an OMS incident to deal with those customers still left off supply once the automation sequence has minimised the area affected. Therefore, the DMS can and does include intelligent automation outages within the reports when it is appropriate to do so, and the DMS network model is correctly updated with actual switch positions in real time. There are still occasions when it is prudent to switch off the automation feature but in a centralised automation system this can be done directly from the control room with no need to visit the site. Having removed all the potential objections to intelligent automation, its deployment across thousands of circuits enables usually half or two thirds of customers on the tripped feeder to be restored in under three minutes, decimating the customer minutes lost targets and gaining millions in rewards for the utility companies.

The third of the shocks to the industry is the response to the threats of climate change. As the future route to zero carbon sustainable economies develops, electricity increases in relative importance because electricity is the alternative solution to most of the situations that use fossil fuels today. Electric vehicles, electric trains, heat pumps replacing oil or gas boilers for heating, electricity replacing gas for cooking will all increase demand for electricity. It will also increase customer's dependence on electricity and, therefore, leads to increased expectations of reliability and availability of supply. Even with intelligent automation deployed within the ADMS functions, the best CML performances in UK today are around 30 to 35 Customer Minutes Lost per connected customer per year. Back in 1990 the best companies were obtaining CML between 90 and 100. In future the CML needs to be three to five, and this needs:

- A redesign of the MV and LV network.
- A massive increase in local renewable microgeneration.
- A massive investment in local energy storage solutions.
- Removal of overhead lines from the MV and LV networks.
- A much-enhanced capability to rebalance the loads across the three phases in the LV network.

Failure to implement these changes does not mean we remain at status quo. Electric cars and embedded generation are increasing imbalance in the networks already and this will start to cause trips and losses of supply and the reliability performance is under threat of worsening.

The innovations to meet new climate change targets are being applied to the network. Lots of solar and wind power generation have been connected and more is in the pipeline, but even the current level of renewable generation is causing issues with control and ensuring sufficient supply. The ADMS software has added ANM, Active Network Management, in recognition that the nature of the distribution network has changed from a mono directional power flow through a passive network to a multi directional power flow through a highly active network. This is in essence an outage avoidance function, taking early measures to constrain generation within network limits preventing an overload trip to customer supplies. However ANM is merely a means to protect the network assets, and while this is an essential function, it does nothing to encourage more embedded renewable energy generation. The preferred, less wasteful approach, is to find uses for the generation at some network point closer to the generation site before it causes the network constraint. The inherent mismatch between intermittent renewable energy supply and a customer generated demand curve is leading towards new methodologies to manage loads as well as generators within the distribution networks. The potential solution requires to combine renewable generator management with energy storage management, such as domestic to utility scale batteries and pumped storage hydro generation, and to manipulate customer demand through demand response programmes. The scope of this challenge dwarfs the capabilities of traditional remote control via SCADA, there are millions of premises capable of installing solar panels and farms installing micro-sized wind power, and these same million premises need demand response controlling techniques and communication technologies. The ADMS industry is currently grappling with these expanding and novel controlling functions, and the solutions will emerge in the fullness of time. Functions such as OMS, outage management, are now being complemented by functions which assist with outage AVOIDANCE, and it is by introducing outage avoidance strategies that CML can be reduced down to the proposed lower target levels that customers will come to expect as they come to depend on the availability of electricity as much as they depend on food, water and shelter.

LV network control, the ability to improve visibility and understanding of what is happening on the LV network is another area where ADMS is extending in response to climate change initiatives.

On line network analysis, requires to deploy an interface to smart meter technology to create accurate load profiles and quantify embedded micro generation either as a negative load within the traditional load profile or as a complementary generation demand profile alongside the load profile.

Mobile and NMS functions requires development to assist crews in collaboratively controlling the LV network between themselves, to avoid a large cost in providing a centralised control of such a massive network over ten times bigger than the MV network.

These are just some of the new directions in which ADMS is developing and as soon as this version of this book is finished, it will become an historical snapshot of this moment in time, and new events will be met by newly developed functions into the future.

The ADMS started life as one function in early 1990s. This has been a thirty year collaboration between an industry and the software programming experts of the emerging Age of Information to produce a formidable system supporting multiple integrated functions for managing the operation of electricity distribution networks. Through the thirty years, the computing technology itself changed at an incredible pace and the electricity industry changed faster than ever before in its history. What this has shown is that there is no end product, there is just a continuing response to an evolving challenge. This is a photograph of where ADMS is now, this photograph can be put on a shelf next to the photograph of the first steam engine and the first cars, and in another thirty years' time we can look at the photograph and think, *How quaint!*

The End (for now).

Not every one of my peers will agree with all that is portrayed in this book, and I am keen to correct any injustices I may have inadvertently committed, either from my ignorance or my personal bias.

The author is interested in your feedback, please contact me at:

derek.macfarlane@btconnect.com